A Country Doctor

My future wife and I as students. UCW, Cardiff 1947

A Country Doctor

A Lifetime in General Practice

BRIAN FROST-SMITH

HAYLOFT PUBLISHING LTD

First published by Hayloft Publishing Ltd., 2017

A CIP catalogue record for this book is available from the British Library

ISBN 978-1-910237-32-8

Designed, printed and bound in the EU

Hayloft policy is to use papers that are natural, renewable and recyclable products and made from wood grown in sustainable forests. The logging and manufacturing processes are expected to conform to the environmental regulations of the country of origin.

Hayloft Publishing Ltd,
a company registered in England number 4802586
2 Staveley Mill Yard, Staveley, Kendal, LA8 9LR (registered office)
L'Ancien Presbytère, 21460 Corsaint, France (editorial office)

Email: books@hayloft.eu
Tel: 07971 352473
www.hayloft.eu

I would like to thank my family, my children and my grandchildren and the many friends who have encouraged me to write this account of what it was like for me to practise as a family doctor in the first year of the National Health Service.

I have written this book in memory of my wife Marjorie; we were medical students together and we worked together. Her unfailing prudent advice and love, apart from the actual medical assistance she gave to me was ever there when I most needed it. We were married in 1950 and remained together for almost sixty seven years until her death in November 2016. My thoughts were always with her while I was writing.

She was looked after in the last six months of her life with exceptional loving care by the staff and carers at Winters Park Residential Home in Penrith. I am truly grateful to them, and I would like to dedicate this book to them all.

Contents

PREFACE

This account of my working life as a family doctor goes back to the beginning of Aneurin Bevan's National Health Service that started in 1948. I qualified in January 1950 and at that time, like most young doctors going into General Practice we progressed at once from being slightly irresponsible medical students, overnight into staid, duly qualified and responsible medics!

This book tells my story of what happened to me when I stepped into my family doctoring role with little specific GP training. I have tried to portray the humour and the tragedy that go together when encountering family problems. All the stories are drawn from real consultations; but names and places are hidden for reason of confidentiality.

I have tried to show how medical management and treatment of patients at home has changed from being what we were always told was more of an art to becoming a science. The treatment of patients today in our 'high tech' hospitals and modern GP Health Centres is so far removed from what went on over 60 years ago, that surely Aneurin Bevan could not have foreseen these changes.

1

In at the Deep End

I am quite nervous. It is nine o'clock on Tuesday morning early in October 1950. I am acting as locum for Dr Alun Davies and I am taking his morning surgery for the first time in this market town of Tregaron. It is very near to my home where I spent much of my teenage years and it is about twenty miles from Aberystwyth where I went to school. Dr Alun and his uncle were my family doctors, so we know each other very well. He knew that I had recently qualified and that I am waiting to join the RAF as a National Service medical officer. He must have heard locally that I am not working at the moment. He contacted me and asked if I would like to act as his locum so that he could take a holiday and go to London to see the Motor Show. I was very pleased to be asked and to have the opportunity to get a little experience. Also, I was in dire need of earning some money so that Marjorie and I could pay the visit to the Lake District for a short holiday that we had planned.

Here I am, in the front parlour of the general grocery store, Rhydronnen, in the market place in this small country market town of Tregaron and I am about to see my first patient. I do not know quite what to expect because although I am now a qualified doctor and I have been well trained, this is the first time that I have been let loose in the field of General Practice. I qualified as a doctor almost six months ago at the Welsh National School of Medicine; part of the University of Wales at Cardiff and for the last six months I have been a junior house doctor working on a surgical ward at Walton Hospital in Liverpool.

చ్రిజ్రిజ్రిజ్రిజ్రిజ్రి

A very junior doctor in his or her first job is closely monitored and supervised. You do not have to take any important decisions nor have you to carry out any new procedures on your own initiative.

'Have you done a cut down?' my Registrar asked me when I appeared

9

in the afternoon of my first day in the job.

'By the way' he said 'I have been waiting all morning; where have you been?'

'Er – no,' I said not quite knowing what a cut down was. I thought rather vaguely that it had something to do with my salary as a Houseman. That was already a pittance being about six or seven pounds a week. Surely it was not to be reduced because I had missed part of the first morning!

'A cut down' he said is when you cannot find a suitable vein in which to insert a needle in order to give intravenous injections or transfusions; so you have to cut the skin over a vein. The saphenous vein just above the ankle is the best one. You expose this big vein that is lying superficially by cutting down to it. Then you can insert a cannula and fix it in place with plaster.'

'Right' I said, 'please show me.' I was not in the least bothered about blood and cutting etc having spent my teenage years on the farm at Broncaradog, belonging to my Uncle Tom and watching the pig being killed and various other rather brutal operative procedures like castrations and tail docking without an aesthetic; that is to say, without the animal having an anaesthetic, which was very common. So I watched while he showed me how it is done. 'This is a doddle' I thought. 'You just have to be careful not to cut the vein when you cut down through the skin. If you do, you are in real trouble.'

He was a pleasant man. My boss, I mean, not the patient – who was probably a long suffering man. Roger was about six years my senior and showed me how to do everything. That was just as well because on leaving medical school I had had a very broad education in all aspects of medicine, but it was all very theoretical and very little, or no practical experience, except in obstetrics. I had had plenty of chances to deliver babies and carry out all the procedures that went with that.

We were taught very clearly how to take a history and examine a patient; how to make a diagnosis and how to supervise treatment. My training did not show me how to remove a sebacious cyst or an ingrowing toe nail, or, for that matter how to do a cut down!

'Calling Dr Frost-Smith.' That's me and that's the tannoy. This is the way that a doctor was summoned to the ward or to an emergency in those days at Walton Hospital. No discreet paging; no mobile 'phones. 'Oh my!' I thought; there are two Dr Frost-Smiths. Marjorie has taken my name when we married nine months ago. These days in the twenty-first century, married professional women often retain their maiden name. Not so common then. I must tell them in the office straight away so that they know that there is a doctor Marjorie and a doctor Brian. I must also respond to the call. 'Doctor Frost-Smith to T ward please.'

The Sister on T Ward calls me over to the bedside of a patient who doesn't look at all happy.

'Mr Teeshay has just come off the Chinese boat that has docked in Liverpool. He has abdominal pain and is complaining of constipation. 'What shall we do?' she asks me. I sit on his bed. 'Please don't sit on the bed doctor,' I jump up hastily and a chair is produced while a retinue of a staff nurse and a probationer stand behind Sister looking at me expectantly as if I am just about to pull a magical fairy out of my pocket. But I am just reaching for my glasses to give me time to think.

'Hello' I say brightly, 'Have you got a pain?'

'He can't speak English,' they all chorus.

'Since he has been in the ward, he has not passed any faeces' says the Sister, 'nor,' she adds 'has he passed any wind.'

'How do you know' I ask, 'have you been with him all the time?' He probably has a bowel obstruction I am thinking. 'Has he vomited?'

'Yes' says Sister, 'some smelly dark material.'

Abdominal pain, dry tongue, vomiting faecal material. I get him to lie flat and examine his abdomen: he wriggles and groans when I gently palpate. No strangulated hernia, no faeces on rectal examination.

I apply my stethoscope to his abdomen and listen to the tremendous volume of *borborygmi* – bowel sounds. That settles it, I think. He almost certainly has an obstructed bowel.

There is no such thing as an Ultra Sound Scan in those days. This little drama, though not so little for Mr Teeshay occurred at 9pm and there are no resident radiographers and no resident laboratory technicians at this time of night; though they can be called in if it is essential.

I call my immediate boss, Roger. He examines the patient, agrees the probable diagnosis with me and says: ' We'll take him to theatre and do a laparotomy.' That is an exploratory incision, opening the abdomen to see what is going on.

'Has he had anything to eat?' he asks Sister.

'He's been in the hospital for the last three hours, so effectively, no, nothing but drinks of water that he vomited back.'

That's okay then so he gives instructions about the pre-op preparation and then we wait for Mr Teeshay to appear in the operating theatre where the anaesthetist is waiting. There the diagnosis is proved correct and the obstruction relieved by a temporary colostomy: that is, bringing the bowel opening out onto the surface of the abdomen. Later he will be assessed to consider a more permanent cure.

ﻌﻟ ﻌﻟ ﻌﻟ ﻌﻟ ﻌﻟ ﻌﻟ ﻌﻟ

So, back to the present, I have stopped day dreaming and I am back in Rhydronnen, the grocery shop in the market square at Tregaron. I have been thinking back over the last six months. But it's no good dreaming; here I am in a General Practice in Aneurin Bevan's National Health Service as it was then, just two years old!

There's one good thing about the NHS: I don't have to worry about charging patients. It's all free: no prescription charges. All the medicines and services are provided free, at the point of use, as they say nowadays. I did ask Dr Alun's aunt, who runs the house for him while he is away, what had happened before the start of the NHS two years ago. She was vague but she said that only a portion of the bills sent out were paid; but patients brought in produce to compensate if they couldn't pay. That was General Practice then.

Now I am here and this is what I wanted to do. I didn't want to specialise I wanted to work in General Practice; visiting people in their homes, making contact with family. All right: how many patients are there waiting ready to call me any time of day or night? Oh, only about three thousand! Well, when I was a student on the ward and the Consultant: Dr Byron Evans stood by the bedside, held the patient's notes in his hand, looked at the patient and then looked at me.

'What is the name of this patient, Doctor?'

He always called the students 'Doctor'. He did it to reassure the patient that we were budding medics and not some strangers who had wandered into the ward. I stammered. I couldn't remember. He had the notes

12

in his hand. I couldn't see the name. He could read the name and read my hesitation in my face. Dr Byron Evans had a slight stammer. He used it to his advantage. He was a first class cardiologist and an excellent teacher.

'How m-m-many p-p-patients have you g-g-got doctor?' he said.

I looked down the ward. 'Five I think sir.'

'Just five only,' he said. 'What will you d-do when you have three th-th-thousand? They will expect you to remember them all.'

'Oh My God, that is where I am now'.

Tuesday Morning

Back to the present: It is 9 o'clock on Tuesday morning in October 1950 and I was fearing the worst, standing in the front parlour of Rhydronnen, the general grocer's shop in the square in Tregaron waiting for my first patient. I did not have to wait long. An elderly lady came in looking at me rather suspiciously. I could hear the hum of conversation coming from the grocer shop adjacent to the parlour where I was to see my patients. It was market day and any one who wanted a consultation with the doctor, entered the shop and while waiting to see the doctor, could buy the groceries and chat to the other customers or prospective patients, as the case may be.

'Where's the doctor then?' she asked with a pronounced Welsh accent and a lilt to her voice.

'Oh,' I said not quite expecting this. 'Dr Alun is away. I think he's gone to London,' I said.

'Oh I know,' she said 'it's the Motor Show isn't it?'

I didn't want to enter into this exchange.

'I think he may have gone to the Motor Show,' I said, 'but what can I do to help you; could you give me your name?' I asked.

'I am Mrs Hannah Watkins,' she said and 'it's this cough that's troubling me, especially at night.'

'How long have you had the cough?' I asked.

'Well,' she said, 'my sister came to see me last Monday. No it wasn't, it was a week last Monday. We had this cow, you see and it was ready to calve but it was in difficulty.

'My husband said: "we'd better call the vet."'

'My sister's coming,' I said.

'"Well what has that to do with it?" he said.

'I've got to go and meet her off the train, so how will you get to the vet?

'"I'll go to the 'phone box in the village and 'phone for him from there," said he.'

I sighed. This was going to be a long consultation.

'Did the cow calve alright?' I asked. 'But more importantly was that when your cough started?'

'Well' she said, 'I think so. My sister said: "What you doin' with that cough, Hanny?" that's what she calls me see. "You'd better go to the doctor or you might end up with the consumption; it's in our family you know. Aunty Myfanwy died in Tregaron Sanatorium, so you'd better be careful."

'Plain speaking, she was, my sister. Always bullying me. So that's why I'm here.'

'Are you coughing up any sputum?'

'What's that?' she asked.

'You know, spit.'

'I don't know, somethin's coming up.'

'Is it coloured?' I asked.

'I need to take your temperature' I said. So I produced my thermometer calibrated, of course, in those days in Fahrenheit and looked at it. The mercury was well down 94°. These days thermometers are not filled with mercury because it is so toxic, and if the thermometer is broken while in the patient's mouth, the mercury could get ingested.

'Would you open your mouth?' I asked. She did and I popped the thermometer in under her tongue. These days, I understand, electronic thermometers are used and are placed in the ear, much better, and time-saving, especially for a busy nurse on the ward in hospital.

I took her wrist and felt her pulse. After about two minutes I looked at the thermometer and it was reading 99°. 'You have got a fever' I said.

'Yes' she said, 'I knew I had, I felt shivery, I don't need that thing to tell me that.'

I ought to examine her chest, I thought, at the very least. But looking at her all tightly dressed up against the cold, layer upon layer of black

The front parlour in the grocer shop in Tregaron looked out on the market square, with the Talbot Hotel in the background. This is a photograph taken in 1932, and the boy leaning against his father's car in the foreground is the writer aged six. This was the view from the 'consulting room' in 1932!

wool, I thought it would be difficult.

'I cannot properly examine you here, in the front room of Rhydronnen. I must visit you at home,' I said. 'I'll come and see you on Friday at home and examine your chest properly. I can't do that here very well. In the meantime I'll give you some cough medicine and you can take it three times a day. I'll leave a prescription for you at Huw Evans the chemist and he will send it on the bus to – where do you live?'

'I live at Llanddewi, just up the road. Bryn yr Afon.'

'Yes, I know where Llanddewi is and I'll find your house.'

This lady was about 65 and she had a cough with fever and possibly coloured sputum. The teaching was then that that would warrant a course of antibiotics to deal with infection. In 1950, I think my memory serves me right, there was penicillin – a fairly new drug and magical in its effect and there was the antibacterial sulphonamide developed by May & Baker, sulphapyridine, commonly known as M&B 693. I had been treated with that when I was in school and the doctor who incidentally was Dr Alun's uncle had said that I had pneumonia. The effect was dramatic then. Penicillin, at that time, could be given only by injection. To maintain blood levels it needed to be given four times a day, 200,000 units intramuscularly, and quite a painful injection. Quite a small dose by today's standards. Not a very practical proposition in a remote countryside situation. District nurses did not give injections. They were not insured against claims made against them. It was well known that an intramuscular injection could cause painful or debilitating damage. There were no oral antibiotics; none that I knew of anyway. I will deal with that problem after I have examined her. First: a prescription for some medicine.

'Can you give me Dr Alun's bottle?' she asked. 'It's a good strong one!'

Before he left for London, Alun had briefed me about on-going problems and also he had written and left me a few prescriptions, that I had difficulty in reading, for his favourite remedies for which he knew patients would ask. When I was a student I had to attend a short course in the Infirmary pharmacy. I was asked to stick a label on an eight ounce medicine bottle and write the label. That's easy, I thought. Lick the label and stick it on the bottle: I failed the test!

The pharmacist looked at me in a long suffering way. 'That will not do' he said. 'The label is put on crookedly and it must be two thirds of the way up the bottle. In those days the pharmacist would wrap the bottle in white paper with the flap at the top fixed down with sealing wax. I also had to learn about the different sorts of bottles. Brown or clear glass for medicines to be taken by mouth, brown or green ribbed bottles for lotions, and I think the label on a bottle containing poison had to have a red label with 'Poison not to be taken'. If it was in poor light, you could feel the ribbed bottle and avoid drinking a toxic lotion.

Today's pharmacists have much more important matters to consider than whether a label is on straight! The plethora of powerful drugs, some with possible serious side effects that we, in 1950 had never imagined, are dispensed to patients under the eagle eye of the pharmacist; and he, as well as the doctor will be blamed if something goes wrong, so he has to exercise all his professional knowledge to be certain that was he is handing to the patient is alright.

Dr Alun's cough medicine was one of the standard cough medicines which could be found in the British National Formulary with slight variations to suit the particular needs of the patient. A favourite one was: Ammonium chloride and morphine mixture. In short: mist ammon chlor et morph. All the ingredients measured in grains, ounces, minims, drachms, fluid ounces etc:

Ammonium bicarbonate	3gr
Ammonium chloride	5gr
Tincture of chloroform and morphine	10m
Liquorice liquid extract	10m
Water	to ½ fl oz

(½ fl oz contains about 1/30gr of anhydrous morphine)
Commonly written in often scrawly writing:

R.
M. Ammon Chlor et Morph
Mitte (send) oz viii
sig (label) oz fs tds (take one tablespoon full three times a day)

I wrote out the prescription, Dr Alun's variation of an expectorant cough mixture, and put it aside to take to the local chemist. I would consider what further treatment should be given after I had examined her. I was a little worried about what I would find. After all a fever of 99° on a cold October morning may very well be a much higher fever when the patient warmed up.

'Good morning Mrs Watkins, I will see you on Friday.' With that, she left and went back into the shop. I could hear the hum of voices of the other customers waiting either to come in to see the doctor or to collect their shopping.

A man in the shop was speaking.

'My 'and,' he was saying. 'It's 'urtin like 'ell, and I think it's still bleeding!'

But the rest of the shoppers or patients did not take much notice. They were more concerned about another matter. Someone else said: 'Who is this young doctor then, is he from round here?'

'I think his parents live near Tynygraig,' someone said. 'I was told that he's Mrs Smith's son.'

'That's Jenny Jones of Ffosybleiddied. I know that family well. Related to Williams, Broncaradog.'

'Oh, that's all right then! I'll go in now if it's my turn.'

I rose from my seat to shake the hand of the next patient. A man of about fifty and obviously a farmer.

'Good morning' I said. 'Have you come in to Tregaron for market day.'

'Yes, Bore da, (good morning) and I've come to ask you about this rash.'

'Let me see.' I looked at his quite work worn palms. They were reddened and rough and looked sore.

'It could be something you are handling. Are you in contact with anything new?'

'Well, I did wonder. There's this new fertiliser. I've had a bit of a job with it and I wasn't wearing gloves.'

'That could be it,' I said. 'I would recommend that you do not let it come into contact with your skin, and if you have to deal with it wear some gloves. I will give you some ointment to apply twice a day.'

There were no steroid creams or ointments at this time. I cannot remember hearing of barrier creams.

'If I give you a prescription can you get it from Evans, the chemist?'

'That's fine' he said, 'I hope it does the trick.'

'What is your name?' I asked.

'Alan Richards, my farm is Craig y Bwlch, It's near New Abbey, if you know where that is.' I wrote a prescription for Coal tar and zinc ointment and gave it to him.

'Apply it to your hands twice a day; but the most important thing is to avoid contact with that fertiliser, and use only mild soap to wash. Household washing soaps contain too much alkali. That will irritate your skin and make it sore.'

'I hope the ointment helps,' I added, 'come back to see me if it doesn't improve in a few days. And do be careful what you handle. Your skin is sensitive.'

I had one last patient to see. He had been waiting in the shop, not wanting to join in the local gossip. He was a young man in his twenties,

My great uncle Dr David Williams. Emigrated to USA - Chicago - and told Mother to write to him and that 'Dr Williams, Chicago' would find him! He died in 1942.

dressed in working clothes. He could be a farmer – a gwas (servant) on a local farm.

'Hello, what's your name and what can I do for you?'

'I'm Gareth Thomas and it's my 'and,' he said. 'I've cut it badly by there.' He indicated the back of his hand the whole of which was covered with a bandage stained in blood.

'How did you do that?' I asked.

'I was scything thistles, see, on Cae goron. Luckily it was near the 'ouse, cos I felt quite faint and nearly fell over when it started bleedin'. I ran up to the 'ouse and called for the missus. She came running from the 'ouse when she heard me callin'.

'Gareth, Gareth bach, what have you done now? Oh my God, what have you done to your hand?'

'I cut it on the scythe when I was sharpening it I said.'

'I'll take you to the doctor, come here and let me wash it first. We'll have to go to town on the tractor, Edwin has got the car. It's only a mile it won't take long.'

I took the bloody bandage off and examined the laceration. It was just over an inch long and still bleeding. I retrieved my box with instruments for suturing. Curved needles, silk and cat gut, syringes, hypodermic needles and dressings.

'Have you been immunised against tetanus?'

'No I 'aven't, as far as know.'

'Right, we must see to that too.'

Everything must be boiled up for a few minutes to sterilise needles and syringes. In those days we had no supply of plastic sterile syringes. The needles were used more than once, boiled each time before use; not acceptable today. I took Gareth into the back of the shop where all the tins of food, bottles, and bags of potatoes, etc were stored. There was a table and two chairs, a sink with running cold water and an electric ring.

In those days, the grid system hadn't reached small towns like Tregaron or for that matter Ponrhydfedigaid – Bont, for short – near where I lived. If you 'had the electric' as the locals called it, it was a locally generated supply. Different voltages sometimes in different towns; and very expensive. The Cardiganshire farmers, the 'Cardis' had a probably unfair reputation for being mean and thrifty. One old farmer is reputed to have said about the 'electric.' 'Very useful it is when you are trying to find the candles in the dark!'

All these thoughts made me realise how things were changing in Cardiganshire quite quickly. My mother was one of four sisters brought up on a hill farm called Ffosybleiddied, literally: the last ditch of the wolf. The farm was near a village called Swyddffynnon, where she and her sisters went to school.

Before tuberculin testing of the milking herd started in Cardiganshire, she told me, the small farmer could not officially sell milk. When the sale of milk started as a regular feature for the small farmer, it made a huge difference because the business brought in a regular monthly cheque. Tuberculosis was too common in this part of Wales. Even a small town like Tregaron had its own sanatorium. But there was no specific treatment for TB. That came later and I will describe what happened later. Back to the story; everything was boiled up and I put in two stitches of silk. These would have to be removed in a week. I also gave him 1500 units of tetanus antitoxin. I must say that Gareth nearly keeled over even when he just saw the needles. I have seen many a big strong man go pale and weak at the knees just at the sight of a hypodermic syringe. I was reminded of my old professor of medicine in Cardiff.

'It is essential to keep your hypodermic needles sharp,' Jock Kennedy, our Professor of Medicine told us. 'Push the needle into a cork at an angle and sharpen it with a carborundum stone. That way, you'll keep your needles sharp and you won't lose your patients!'

I put a clean dressing on the wound and told Gareth to return in a week to have the stitches out.

'Mind you keep it clean, now. You'd better wear a glove to protect it. By the way,' I said, 'you're not from this parts of Wales are you?' I could tell from his accent and his constant use of the expression 'By there', and saying 'see' all the time – just as today young folk put in the word 'like' every few words – that he was from South Wales.

'No,' he said. 'I'm from Treorchy. I worked in a shop: selling tobacco, cigarettes and so on. I got fed up with bein' inside all day while my friends were workin' outside. So I said to Mam, "I'm goin' to see if I can get a farming job in Cardiganshire."

'Right, you go', she said, 'if it makes you happy and stops you complainin' all the time.'

'I met Edwin Morris in the Red Lion here in Tregaron see. He farms at Cefn Meurig an' he wanted help on his farm. So here I am. I've been workin' for Edwin and Mrs Morris for six months now, since hay time, gettin' in the gwair. You know what that is, I expect. Gettin' in the hay and the corn is a very important job for farmers in this part of Wales: we get so much rain. The missus looks after me well, see, she brought me here today, no fuss; very kind they are, see.'

'Now Gareth, I'll need to see you in a week to get those two stitches out. Can you do that?'

'Right ho doctor, will it hurt much?'

'No hardly at all, so don't worry. See you in a week.'

I let Gareth go. There was no one else to see this morning, but in the afternoon I have to visit a sort of branch surgery: really little more than a calling place to see patients with minor ailments and to give repeat prescriptions. So on Tuesday and Thursdays I have to go down to a farm at Llangwyryfon in south Cardiganshire. Alun had taken me down there as part of his introduction to the practice. I had to be there at about 2 o'clock. There wouldn't be a lot to do, writing repeat prescriptions; signing certificates, and maybe a minor illness to treat. The thing was; I couldn't remember the way. I knew I had to take the main road, the A465, Tregaron to Bronant, but I had to turn off to the left and wend my way through a series of small roads to get to the farm, Tynarfon where there would be a few patients waiting.

Some time before I started doing this locum, when Alun had asked me to stand in for him, I spoke to my old friend Sam. He was a year ahead of me but I had been at school at Ardwyn with him and now we shared a room in the Medical Students Club. That was a very desirable place to live: in Howard Gardens, near the Infirmary and in close touch with everyone. I asked him what I would need to take with me to do this locum in general practice.

'Oh damn it, look Frost,' he said. 'I did that locum for Dr Alun last year while he went to the Motor Show and I went straight from qualifying. You have nothing to worry about. Don't forget I'd had no experience at all! All you need is a prescription pad, a stethoscope and a car to get around the practice.' This was, perhaps an exaggeration, but roughly true, at that time!

I myself had had no experience in General Practice, just the six months at Walton Hospital as a junior House Surgeon. But this experience was very important as a basis especially then, as it would be very serious to miss the diagnosis of an acute abdominal emergency like an acute appendix or a perforated gastric ulcer! Apart from this valuable starter I just had the basic knowledge in medical training that we all got as students. But I had no problems up to this point.

'Remember,' Sam had said. 'If you are worried about a patient you can always get a domiciliary visit. The consultants in Aberystwyth are only too happy to come out. There is a surgeon and a general physician also a gynaecologist and others, so Alun told me. I can't remember their names, but Alun will tell you. So don't worry Frost. I can tell you, all you need is, as I said, your stethoscope, a fountain pen and a lot of medical common sense and care.'

I must admit that that had cheered me up and after all, I had had a six month spell of very intensive employment as a surgical House Doctor. The thought of back up from the consultants at Aberystwyth was very re-assuring.

So I set off at about half past one after lunch at the Talbot Hotel thinking it might take me about half an hour to get to the farm. I left Marjorie sitting in the lounge at the Talbot. We were expecting our first baby; due in February and Marjorie was knitting and reading, she was quite relaxed and content.

The Talbot had made us very comfortable and had fed us well. There was only one telephone in the hotel, it was in the entrance hall apart from the one in the office. All telephone calls for the doctor would go to Alun's house up on the Lampeter Road. If a patient wanted me, Alun's aunt at the house would have to 'phone the Talbot. If a call from a patient came through for me at night which did not happen often, someone would have to fetch me to the phone.

Alun, considering our situation; that we had only been married six months, and the fact that Marjorie was 'expecting', had generously paid for us to stay in the hotel in the square in Tregaron. We were very comfortable. There were quite a number of interesting guests also staying. One of the big attractions bringing visitors to the area was the Tregaron Bog. An area of special scientific interest to bird watchers and nature enthusiasts generally. We were very fortunate to be so well looked after.

I followed the road out of Tregaron towards Bronant. I was supposed to take a left turn somewhere. I missed the correct turn left and got quite lost, driving around hoping to see the landmark, a very large ash tree near a barn with a red corrugated iron roof. Eventually I saw it with the farm house close by. I knocked briefly and entered. It was a large kitchen with a big log fire in a huge old fireplace. There were four men and a woman sitting around the fire.

'Prynawn Da' (Good afternoon) I said. I could speak very little Welsh although my teenage years had been spent in Wales and at school in

Aberystwyth. They looked at me with some curiosity, wondering, I imagine, whom I could be.

'I'm Dr Frost-Smith,' I said feeling a little nervous. 'I'm standing in for Dr Alun.'

'Oh,' they chorused, not very enthusiastically. 'Where's the doctor then?'

'He's away in London, but I am the doctor now, so can I help you?'

'You look very young to be a doctor,' one of them said. 'Where are you from?'

'My home is Hafod House, Ystrad Meurig.'

'Well that's all right then.'

'Now then,' I said 'who's first?'

One of the men came forward, the rest of the group melted away into the next room.

'Hello, what can I do for you?'

'It's my sustificate. It's due now. Dr Alun gives it to me for a month.'

'What's the matter with you?' I asked.

'It's my back. I work on the farm but I haven't been able to work properly since I fell off the gambo (a two wheeled cart, pulled by a horse) when we were spreading manure last autumn. Doctor gives me tablets, but they're not much good.'

'What are the tablets?'

'I don't know, they're little white ones. They're supposed to be strong, but they don't seem to help at all.'

'How old are you?'

'Forty eight, I feel more like a hundred!'

'Where d'you get the pain?'

'Just here,' he said pointing to the lumbar area of his back.

'I need to take a look. Can you pull your shirt up?'

He stood rather awkwardly and I felt the area. Then I gave it a small thump with my rolled up fist.

'Ow! that hurt a bit.'

'Just bend over.'

'I can only go so far'

He had bent very little. 'Is there a couch here that you can lie on for me to test your back?'

'Ask Olwen if we can go in the parlour, there's a couch there, if that will do.'

'What's your name?' I asked.

'Dafydd Meredith, I have the farm at Tyn y Bwlch.'

I went through into the kitchen.

'Olwen, can we use the couch in your parlour. I want Dafydd to lie down so I can examine him?'

'Yes, I'll show you: in here. There you are, that will be quite all right. Come in here Dai, the doctor wants to examine you.'

With Dafydd Meredith lying flat on his back, I was able to test his straight leg raising. It was very limited especially on the right side. Some pressure on the sciatic nerve I thought.

'I think you may have a disc lesion' I said. 'You may need to see a specialist, an orthopaedic surgeon.'

'Doctor said he is going to send me if it's no better.'

'Right, Mr Meredith, I'll give you the usual certificate.'

I made out the NHS certificate for four weeks and gave it to him.

'You'll come back to see Doctor Alun in a month then, won't you, and he'll decide whom to send you to.'

'Thank you doctor,' he said and went out.

I asked the next patient to come in. Mrs Myfanwy Jenkins, a woman of about fifty, I guessed.

'How can I help you?' I asked. She looked very pale and I was concerned.

'I'm not feeling at all well doctor,' she said. 'I've no energy and I can't do my work properly.'

'What work do you do?'

'Well, me and my husband live at Penderlwn Wen. It's a small farm only about thirty acres, a smallholding really. We just have two cows, a pig, a gander and two geese. Also some hens and a cockerel. My husband has the farm, but he works as a Road Man. I expect you know how hard that work is: keeping our roadsides tidy, it's really a full time job. He helps me but, I must keep the farm going.'

His job, as I understood it, was very common indeed, then. He would keep a certain stretch of road tidy; keeping the verges clean and the hedges and roadside grass clipped. These men were called Length Men in England, because they had a fixed length of road that it was their job to keep tidy. Very often in Cardiganshire and possibly elsewhere the husband would have his job and receive a regular wage from the council, while his wife would run the smallholding, usually twenty to thirty acres. Nowadays, machinery has taken over. One can see the tractor with the huge grass and hedge cutter moving slowly along the road and doing the same job as the Road Man used to do.

I knew several families where this was the situation. Both husband and wife worked hard and lived off the land with one or two animals. It was very hard work for both. In most of the instances that I knew of, they would have no running water in the house. Water would be collected in a bucket from the pistyll, the water spout with drinking water coming out of the bank. Seldom was there a well; and a rainwater butt would supply water for washing. Any hot water would come from the kettle on the fire. The lavatory was the Ty Bach, literally the small house at the bottom of the garden! Lighting was a paraffin lamp and candles. Families like this, as I know well, had a good productive garden with root and green vegetables, fruit trees and fruit bushes.

'How long have you felt like this?' I asked.

'Well Doctor, I am fifty one, so I know I'm at the change, and I didn't expect to feel as bad as this. I think this terrible feeling of no energy has been coming on for a long time. I've been losing a lot, you know at my time of the month. D'you know what I mean. You're very young, d'you understand me?'

'Yes I know exactly what you mean.'

I looked at her conjunctivae. They were pale, as were her finger nails. Her cheeks were pink, but where did that colour come from?

'I must examine your tummy. I'll ask Olwen for the use of the couch again.'

With Myfanwy lying down and quite relaxed; and she was good at relaxing as many women are when it comes to a medical procedures. Unlike many men, who tense up and even faint at the sight of a doctor or an injection needle like Gareth Thomas, the patient I saw earlier in Tregaron.

I felt her abdomen carefully. There was no tenderness or rigidity but I think I could feel a slight uterine enlargement. Very slight, like a twelve to fourteen week pregnancy, but certainly not that at fifty one years old.

'I am going to get a specialist to see you,' I said.

'O Mawredd (Oh Glory) I can't do that, I've got to see to the farm and there's Alyn my son, he's only twelve. He can't do the work at home. He'll be just coming home from school now. He'll wonder where I am.'

'No, no, Myfanwy,' I said. ' Calm down. I'm not proposing to send you anywhere today.'

'Well what are you wanting me to do?'

'I'm going to bring a specialist, a gynaecologist, out to see you at home. Your womb is a little enlarged I think and we must find out what is going on.'

'I don't know what you're thinking about. I can't pay for that sort of thing. I've got to pay the rent on the farm next week. Just leave it; I'll have to manage somehow. Give me a good tonic to buck me up a little.'

'Myfanwy, Myfanwy! Don't you know there's a free health eervice now – the NHS. This is 1950. You won't have to pay a penny for this service.'

'I can't go to the 'ospital now.'

'You don't have to go anywhere. I'm going to bring the specialist out to see you at home, hopefully tomorrow, or in the next day or so. Have you got a relative somewhere near here, apart from your husband, I mean.'

'My sister Megan, she has the Post Office in Llangwyryfon, so she has the telephone.'

'I am going back to Tregaron now. I'll telephone the specialist and see if he can come in the next day or so. Probably it will be Friday. You go home now and tell your husband what is happening. I will 'phone your sister as soon as I know the time he is coming and we will meet you at your sister's house: the post office at Llangwyryfon.'

I left the farmhouse having thanked Olwen and returned to Tregaron. Alun had given me the telephone numbers of the consultants in Aberystwyth that I might need. I wanted to talk to Mr Williams the gynae consultant. So I phoned his secretary at the hospital.

'Hello, this is Dr Brian Frost-Smith from Tregaron, Dr Alun Davies' practice. I would like to speak to Mr Williams please, if he's around.'

'Oh he's here now, you've just caught him. I'll put you through to him.'

'Jim Williams, Gynaecology, hello.'

'Hello Mr Williams. I'm Dr Brian Frost-Smith. I'm doing locum for Dr Alun Davies in Tregaron.'

'Oh hello. As a matter of fact Alun did mention to me that he was taking a couple of weeks off. It's Motor Show time isn't it? He's not going to buy yet another car is he? How many has he got?

'Three I think,' said I. 'He's got that big Ford Pilot, as well as the Hillman Minx and the Ford Prefect. That's the one I'm allowed to drive! It's a good little car and very reliable. What you need in a country practice.'

'What can I do for you?'

'I saw this patient this afternoon at Llangwyryfon. She looked ill and had obviously been losing heavily at her irregular periods. But I thought I could just feel the uterus abdominally. It's difficult to examine a patient properly in a farm kitchen and I was concerned.'

'Rightly so, my boy. What would you like me to do?'

'Well, could you come out on a domicilliary visit, as I say she's at Llangwyryfon. She's going to be at her sister's house. That's the Post Office in the middle of the village. So it's easy to locate.'

'Let me see now: I'm afraid I won't be able to meet you until Friday morning I've got to be in the ward here at nine o'clock   tomorrow and then I've got outpatients in clinic for most of the rest of the day. But I could meet you at Llangwyryfon at about eleven thirty to twelve on Friday. How would that do?'

'That's marvellous, I look forward to meeting you. I'll ring the family at the Post Office to let them know. Goodbye and thanks.'

I felt much happier now that had been arranged and I returned to the Talbot for our evening meal. I was telling Marjorie all about my day out in the wilds of Cardiganshire. I told her about Myfanwy.

'That could be serious,' said she, 'very serious. You certainly did right to refer her. Oh gosh, with a bulky uterus, I just hope it's not something malignant. Could be, you know.

'I'm sure he'll want to take her in to curette the uterus – a D and C you know. We'll know in a few days when that's done. In the meantime I've got this other woman with a bad chest in Llanddewi. That could be serious too.'

'Well, this is the life you wanted isn't it. You'll have to gain a lot more experience in GP before you can be let loose on your own. Then you've still got your National Service to do. You might get a bit of experience in the army or RAF.'

'I've had my preliminary medical for call up. Do you remember I had to go down to a grotty place in Walton Road, Liverpool?'

We had a good meal that evening: roast pheasant and a trifle to follow. We went to bed at about ten o'clock and slept until we were woken by a knock on the bedroom door. 'Telephone for you doctor, it's in the hall. I'll tell them to hold on.' I looked at my watch. Ten past one! 'Right I'm coming.'

Early hours Wednesday morning

I picked up the receiver. 'Is that the doctor?' said a strange voice.

'Yes, it's Dr Frost-Smith speaking. Dr Alun is away you know.'

'Yes, he did tell me that he was intending to go to the Motor Show in London.'

'Well can I help you?'

'Yes, I'm afraid my wife is ill. I'm sorry to call at this time but I'm worried about her.'

'What is your name?'

'I am Terrence Kilmannon, and my wife is Sheila.'

'What's the trouble?'

'She's complaining of pains in her stomach and she's been sick as well.'

'Oh dear, I think I'd better come and see her. Where do you live?'

'It's about two miles from Tregaron on the Lampeter road. It's a bungalow on the right, The name is on the front gate: Westralia.'

'Right I'll come straight away.'

'I'll leave the light on in the porch so you'll easily see it.'

That's a strange name for a house in Wales, I thought. Well we'll soon find out more. It was a pleasant evening and the moon lit up the landscape. Trees with hardly any leaves; autumn was well on its way.

After I had driven about a mile from town on the Lampeter road I saw a light in a bungalow on the right hand side. That must be it, I thought. I pulled over to the edge of the road and got out of the car; I walked up to the front door and knocked. A man came to the door dressed in a red dressing gown. He looked very anxious but he was obviously pleased to see me.

'Good evening doctor,' he said with a smile. 'I am Terry Kilmannon. It's so good of you to come out at this time of night, but I am very worried about my missus.'

'Well,' I said, 'tell me about it.'

'Sheila it is' he said. 'She was quite alright yesterday and we went into Lampeter as usual for our shopping. It's market day on Tuesdays you know and it's usually very busy. But we got the bus in to town and did our shopping in the Co-op. Then we went and had our lunch in the café that is opposite. I had a poached egg on toast, but Sheila said she was hungry and chose some fish and chips. I must say she didn't seem to enjoy it and she left some of it.'

'Never mind' she said, 'we'll have a proper tea when we get home.'

'The fish and chips were very greasy and I said: 'I don't think I like this place.'

'Well don't make a fuss,' said she. 'Let's go and get the bus home.'

'When we got home we sat for a bit listening to the wireless. We're lucky, we have a very good wireless. We do have electricity here, it's generated in the power station in Tregaron. But our wireless works from a battery. I think it needs a new high tension battery, the big one, you know, and we have to get the accumulator charged every week in Hugh Morgan's garage in Tregaron.

'That is really nothing to do with it except that Sheila said she was tired and went to bed quite early. I went soon after. It was around midnight when I was woken by Sheila groaning. Then she suddenly got out of bed and rushed to the lavatory. I heard her retching and vomiting. I went to the bathroom and found her lying on the floor. 'Whatever has happened?' I asked.

'Oh Terry I feel awful; I've got a pain in my stomach and I feel so ill.'

'Look here, come to bed and I'll call the doctor.'

'Oh dear I think you had better,' she said.

'You lie down while I go to the telephone.' So that's what happened.'

'Well,' I said, 'Let me see her.'

'Come to the bedroom, she's in her bed.' She was lying in bed looking rather pale.

'Hello Mrs Kilmannon, I'm Dr Frost-Smith. How are you feeling now?'

'Hello doctor, I'm Sheila Kilmannon. I am sorry to call you out this time of night. As a matter of fact I'm feeling a little better.'

'How old are you Sheila?'

'I'm sixty four; well to be truthful I'll be sixty four next month.'

'Show me your tongue,' I said. It was coated and dry. Her pulse was eighty per minute, regular and good volume.

'Just lie back and let me see your stomach.'

Her abdominal wall was moving with her breathing. I palpated gently all around paying particular attention to the Macburney point overlying the appendix. That is the point lying one third of the way along a line joining the spine of the ilium to the umbilicus. Mind you, that line could end up somewhere around the left knee in a very obese person!

There was no tenderness or rigidity over the appendix area. But when I palpated in the area in the front on the right side just under the ribs she tensed and groaned.

'Oh that hurts, doctor.' I thought I could feel a small mass under my fingers. Gall bladder came to my mind immediately. Now, I thought, I must complete this examination properly to exclude appendicitis. A rectal examination did not reveal any tenderness. She had no fever and had not been particularly constipated.

'Sheila, I think you have gallstones' I said.

'Well,' she said 'that's funny. I saw a doctor in Australia just over a year ago. I had had a very bad pain like a colic just there where you were pressing. He said it could very well be stones in my gall bladder. He said I had better go to a doctor if I suffered from the same sort of pain again. But that fish and chips I had for dinner was very greasy. Could that have brought this on do you think?

'Well' I said, 'I can't be sure about that. But it's more than likely. But I am sure about two things. I must refer you to a specialist, and he will doubtless ask for a cholecystogram.'

'What in heaven's name is that?' she asked.

'Well it's a special X-ray. They will give you an injection into your blood that contains a special substance and when they take the X-ray of your stomach, the gall bladder will show up on it and they will be able to detect any stones in it. I will write and ask for an appointment for you to see the specialist and they will send an appointment to you, to attend the clinic in Aberystwyth Hospital'.

'Goodness me, how am I going to get to Aber for the appointment?'

'Now don't you worry Cariad,' (sweetheart) said Terence. 'We can get the bus to Tregaron and the train to Aberystwyth from there.'

'Now, how do you feel? Has the pain gone? And are you still feeling very sick?'

'No I'm feeling much better, I think I'll be able to sleep now.'

'The second thing is: I will call to see you tomorrow morning at about ten o'clock. Oh goodness me, what is the time?' I looked at my watch: 'Three o'clock in the morning – I will of course see you later today. By then I will have phoned the hospital about your appointment and I will be able to tell you what they say.'

On the way back to Tregaron I was thinking about the last few months of my time at Walton Hospital. Marjorie was pregnant and expecting our first baby. She was about three months pregnant. She had been working at the hospital as a House Physician on what was called Block Two. This was a separate building from the main hospital and was devoted entirely to patients with tuberculosis. They were all treated conservatively with rest. I am not sure, but I do not think they were receiving streptomycin which was fairly new. This antibiotic had been used to treat children with tuberculous meningitis for a year or two with great success. But for pulmonary tuberculosis, isonyazid and para amino salicylic acid, two drugs that were to change, with great success the treatment of pulmonary TB were not being used as yet at Walton Hospital; as far as I remember – more on that later.

Once a week, there was a real time X-ray screening session for selected patients on Block Two, to assess their progress. The doctors and some nurses would attend and Dr Coran the Medical Registrar would be in charge.

The patient's X-ray would be looked at 'live', or 'real time' as they call it now, on the screen so all those present were supposed to wear protective aprons. Marjorie told me that there were often not enough aprons for every one present. She said that frequently she was not given one!

I think it was in August that she started threatening miscarriage. It was very severe and she saw the consultant obstetrician who told her to go home and rest. It all settled down with the treatment and rest, but what had caused it? I found myself thinking much later.

Dr Coran, the Registrar on Block Two was a pleasant young man of about thirty five. He was Jewish. He told Marjorie that when he left school, his father had said to him, 'Well, my boy. What career are you going to choose: Medicine, the Army, Law or the Church!'

I had chosen Medicine as my career, I would still have to serve in the armed forces, but I would serve as a doctor.

I knew that my 'call up' order for National Service would soon arrive. This had been deferred to allow me to complete my medical training; just as well for me, and the armed services; I would not have been much use as a soldier! If I had been called up at the age of eighteen, I would probably have ended up in Burma as a Japanese Prisoner of War. And we all know what happened to them, and how they suffered.

So it was no surprise when an official looking envelope arrived one morning. It was to tell me that I must attend at the Service Recruiting Office at 228 Walton Road at 9.30am on the 24 August. I arrived at the time and day of the appointment. It was an old three story building on the main Walton Road. I entered a large room on the ground floor milling with young men half dressed waiting to be called in for their medical examination for the armed services. There was quite a smell too of unwashed or sweaty bodies.

A man came up to me and said: 'This way, get your shirt off and stand over there with those other boys!'

'I'm Dr Frost-Smith,' I said.

'Oh' said he, 'you'd better come with me.'

He lead me upstairs and knocked on a door. I was ushered into a quieter room where a man in a white coat was sitting at a desk.

'Hello' he said, 'come in.' He shuffled with some papers on the desk and looked at me.

'Are you Dr Brian Meredith Frost-Smith?' he asked. 'Where are you working just now?'

'I'm surgical House man at Walton Hospital.'

'Well,' he said, 'I'm Dr Thornton. I'm retired from the Indian Army and they've given me this job to do. Examining hundreds of fit young men for National Service Duties. You'll have to strip off, I've got to make sure you're all in one piece. You can put your clothes on that chair and come over here and lie on the couch.'

I did as I was asked and he palpated my abdomen and listened to my heart and lungs. 'All right' he said, 'nothing much wrong with you is there! Hullo! what's this?'

He had spotted a red patch on my right ankle. It was an itchy red area I had had for some months. I couldn't stop scratching it.

'It's just a scratch rash. It itches like hell!'

'Well just you get it seen to my boy. Any patient of yours who noticed it would say 'Physician Heal Thy Self'. Now stand up.'

He grasped me in the crotch and said 'Cough!' I did so. 'Okay, no Inguinal Hernia' he said. 'Bend over' He took a quick look at my backside. 'No haemorrhoids. Fit A1 as far as I can see. You will have another medical,' he said. 'Which service have you asked to enter?'

'The RAF' I replied.

'Then you'll be seen again in London at Air ministry.'

'Marvellous life in the services, my boy. I joined when I was thirty and went straight into the Indian Army. Wonderful life! Retired at fifty five and went into practice. Good Luck to you! Good morning.'

He was a dapper little man, short with iron grey crinkly hair, a small military moustache and a smart tweed suit. And there was I in my old grey flannels worn out sports coat and my shirt with a threadbare collar. What a sight. He must have wondered what the young doctor was coming to these days. But the pay awarded to House doctors in their first job was small, and I certainly couldn't afford to buy good expensive clothes.

When I first went into General Practice, I was expected to wear a suit, and of course, a collar and tie. So I wore an expensive Harris Tweed hand made suit. A gift from Marjorie's mother!

That was the end of that 'call up' medical adventure. But I was sorry for the crowd of lads waiting to be seen. I had had a sort of VIP treatment as a medic, but they would just be pushed through like cattle. Later I had experience on the other side of the counter as a service Medical Officer. That was very boring work as you can imagine, examining dozens of healthy young men. At the same time you had to have your wits about you, ready to spot a not too obvious abnormality like a perforated ear drum. So, back to Tregaron!

Wednesday Morning

I planned to visit Sheila Kilmannon at about 10am, but first I must 'phone the hospital about her appointment and ask them about transport. I don't have to go to meet the gynae specialist until Friday at about 11.45 at Langwyryfon Post Office. First I must 'phone Myfanwy's sister, Megan, at the Post Office.

'Hello, Langwyryfon Post Office, Megan Morris speaking.'

'Good morning Mrs Morris. I'm Dr Frost-Smith, Dr Alun's Locum.'

'Oh yes doctor. Megan has told me about the appointment with the specialist. I'm so glad that you're doing something. She's been quite unwell and I've been so worried about her.'

'Well, Mr Williams is coming to see her at your house on Friday morning at about eleven thirty.'

'Yes, that is quick! What will you need? And is this specialist a doctor.'

'Oh yes, He's a surgeon who deals with women's complaints. All surgeons call themselves 'Mr' you know. It's a hang over from long ago in the nineteenth century, when all surgeons were barbers.'

'We'll just need a private room with a bed so he can examine her.'

'Oh Pob peth yn iawn (everything is in order). I'll expect you later. Bore da.'

I drove to Trevor and Sheila's bungalow, Westralia. Trevor greeted me warmly.

'She's had a good sleep and she's feeling much better. I've kept her in bed so that you can examine her.'

Sheila looked much better. 'Good morning' I said, 'how are you feeling today?'

'Oh I feel one hundred per cent,' said she. 'Is it really necessary for me to go and see this doctor in Aber.'

'Now then Sheila,' said Terry, 'if the doctor says it's necessary we must do as he says.'

'I've been on to the appointments at the hospital,' I said 'and they have made an appointment for you to see Mr Blenavon at two o'clock on 15 October. He is a consultant surgeon. I'm afraid they couldn't promise transport. Now I've written a letter to Mr Blenavon giving him all the details of your case. They will send you confirmation of your appointment. You must let me know if there are any problems.'

'By the way, how did you arrive at the name Westralia for your bungalow? I noticed that you mentioned seeing a doctor in Australia; were you there on holiday?'

'Oh my goodness no, doctor. We lived just outside Perth. We went there in 1934. I worked in a factory. When the war came and we were fighting the Japs, the factory became a munitions factory making tanks. You've heard of the 'Waltzing Matilda' tank: that was the main thing we produced. We were so happy, but when the war ended we felt we would like to come back to Blighty. So here we are and because we had such a good life in Australia, and the people there were so kind to us we had to call our home here Westralia.'

'Thank you very much for your help, doctor. When we get confirmation of the appointment for Sheila I will let you know.'

It was about ten o'clock when I got back to Tregaron, I needed to find out if there were any calls. I stopped at Alun's house and asked his aunt if anyone had phoned with a message. Miss Davies said that a patient had called, and asked if the doctor would call to see her son who is suffering from asthma.

'Where does she live and what's the name?' I asked.

'Oh it's Mrs Evans, it's quite near, it's out on the road to Bronant. Just near the station but on the other side of the road. There are some new council houses. It's number four Teifi Way. They are quite a big family, I think. They are very good patients, a hard working family. There are four children. The youngest is just a baby girl, and there are three others, all boys at school. It's one of them that has the asthma.'

'Right,' I said. 'I'll do that call now and on the way back I'll call here again to see if there are any more visits to be done.'

It took only a few minutes to get to the house on Teifi Way. On the way I looked at the petrol gauge. I must call at Hugh Morgan's garage for petrol on the way back, I thought. Number four was a neat looking house with a tidy front vegetable garden. I went round to the back, knocked on the kitchen door, went in and called out. 'Hello, it's the doctor.'

After a minute, a woman came hurrying in to the kitchen.

'Oh doctor, I'm glad you walked in and didn't wait at the door. Dr Alun always comes in that way.'

'Hello Mrs Evans, I am Dr Frost-Smith. I'm standing in for the doctor while he is away. I understand one of your boys is not well.'

'It's my eldest son, Thomas, we call him Tommy, he's fourteen and he has had attacks like this before. Dr Alun says it's asthma. He's been playing around his uncle's farm and his aunt Annie got him to go round collecting the eggs. She gives him sixpence when he does little jobs for her. He loves being up there on the farm but it's possible that he has breathed in some dust, maybe some bits of feather. Doctor thought he might be sensitive to feathers so I took the precaution of making sure that his pillow is feather free. But you can't keep him away from the farm, he loves the place.

'He was fine at tea time and he has a healthy appetite like most boys of fourteen. He'd eat me out of house and home if I let him. Then around midnight we could hear him wheezing. He was quite distressed and short of breath. It was really worrying, just to look at him. I gave him the last dose of the medicine he has and he quietened down after a while. He is a little better now but I thought you should see him and perhaps give him some more medicine. I'll take you up to him now.'

Tommy was a fine boy sitting up in bed reading. When he saw me he put the paper down.

'Hallo doctor, I'm feeling much better. Can I get up Mam?'

'Now just you wait 'till the doctor's examined you,' said his mother.

'What are you reading?' I asked.

'Oh, just *The Champion*' said he.

'I used to take that paper, is Rockfist Rogan still winning all his fights?'

'He certainly is!'

'Now then: let's have look at you.' He had no fever and he was not wheezing. I examined his chest and there were no signs of his recent attack.

'How did you feel when you had the attack last night?'

'Oh Duw Duw it was terrible.'

'Peidiwch tyngu please! (don't swear) Tommy bach; not in front of the doctor.' We all laughed.

'Well, sorry Mam, but I thought I was going to die!'

'Okay, Tommy, I'll give you a prescription for some more of the medicine.' I looked at the empty bottle. It was Linctus Scillae Co. 'And some tablets. They're called Franol. Can you collect these from the chemist? You can give him half a tablet if he seems a bit wheezy at night. Just half a tablet mind until we see how he responds. Just once at night. You can continue with the medicine as before. I'll call again at the week end to see how he is getting on.'

'Oh thank you doctor,'

'And Tommy, you just keep away from those birds!'

'Some birds don't have feathers,' he said with a grin.

'Now Tommy,' said his mother, 'just behave yourself.'

On the way back I called at Hugh Morgan's garage for petrol. Dai came out to serve me. He knows who I am because his sister married Alun and she of course is enjoying her visit to London with him while I am standing in for them.

'Hello Dai, how is your father?'

'He's doing very well thank you, doctor; I must call you doctor now mustn't I! Father doesn't do much in the garage though.' I had known Dai since I was a child, when we, as a family would call for petrol.

'It's okay thank you Dai, 'Brian' will do. Could you put in six gallons please. Alun said to charge it to his account'.

'Pob peth un iawn' (Everything is fine).

Wednesday Afternoon

This afternoon, I must visit a patient, Mrs Bethan, a woman who has pernicious anaemia. She lives out on the road towards Pontrhydfendigaid – Bont for short in a cottage called Ty Croeso (Welcome House). She lives alone and it is very important that she has the injection of liver extract regularly. Alun asked me to be sure that she is given her injection on Wednesday.

Pernicious anaemia is a disease of the blood in which the body fails to produce mature white blood cells. It is a failure to absorb Vitamin B12 essential for the formation of these cells. The vitamin can be taken by mouth but it needs an intrinsic factor in the stomach so that it can be absorbed into the blood. The disease is a failure to produce this intrinsic factor. The disease proves to be fatal without treatment. As recently as the early twentieth century it was discovered that if patients could be persuaded to eat raw liver, regularly, the patient recovered. It had to be raw liver, cooking destroyed the active ingredient. Soon after it was found that liver 'juice', would have the same beneficial effect given by mouth and a little later an injectable extract, anahaemin, was isolated.

The patient I was going to see had to be given this injection. Nowadays pure vitamin B12 – cyanobalamin is given.

It is now twelve thirty and time for lunch. I will give Mrs Bethan her injection this afternoon. Back at the Talbot, I found Marjorie waiting and ready for lunch. She had been out for a walk.

'Well,' she asked, 'what have you been seeing this morning, anything interesting?'

I told her about Tommy Evans and his asthma attack. 'Yes', she said, 'There's sometimes an element of tension involved, that's why the Franol is so effective: doesn't it have a very small amount of barbiturate as well as the theophylline'.

'Yes, it does, and that is why some doctors don't like using it. But as you say, it is very effective. I wouldn't mind betting that it will be withdrawn from use one day, as soon as an alternative is found. So apart from the walk what else have you been doing?'

'Believe it or not, I have been trying to knit something for the baby.'

'Well done, but I'm not sure that I can imagine you taking up knitting! Let's have some lunch. I'm hungry and I'm going to have some of their cawl. You know, it's a clear soup made from mutton with a lot of leeks and other vegetables. It's really delicious! What will you have?'

'I've asked and they're going to make me a toasted tomato and cheese sandwich.'

After lunch I drove out of the town on the road to Bont. The cottage Ty Croeso was about two miles down the road on the left. I had already been there with Alun on the day he took me around the practice to introduce me to some patients.

On that day when we called to see Mrs Bethan she had complained of a very painful left wrist.

Alun had looked at it and squeezed it gently where it was swollen. 'Ow' she said, 'that hurts.'

'How did that happen?' he asked.

'The ground was slippery outside this morning and I nearly fell; I put out my hand to save myself and my weight fell on my wrist.'

'Mae wedi tori (it's broken), I'm sure. You will have to go to the hospital to have it set, but in the meantime I'll put a firm bandage on it. I'll have to call for an ambulance to take you.'

'Oh Na, Dim diolch i chi (Oh no, no thank you) I'll get my brother to take me, it will be easier than calling for an ambulance, and quicker. You know my brother don't you. Edwin Morris at Cefn Meurig. Do you think you could tell him what has happened?'

'Yes, we'll call in there on the way back.'

Alun gave Mrs Bethan the injection of Anahaemin. 'Dr Frost-Smith will give you the next one next Wednesday. Your wrist will have been attended to by then,' said he.

So I found Mrs Bethan's cottage. It was built of stone with a well kept garden. I knocked and went in. I found Mrs Bethan sitting by the fire nursing her wrist which was in a sling.

'How's the wrist feeling today?' I asked.

'Oh it's coming on, but it's still quite painful, and as you see I'm right handed so I've got to learn to do everything with my left!'

I looked at her fingers, they were pink and warm. The hospital had put on a dorsal slab of plaster to keep the wrist in the right position. I gave her the injection of anahaemin.

'Is there anything else I can do for you?'

'O no, diolch yn fawr (thank you very much). My brother is calling soon and he will get me anything I need. When I have to go back to the hospital, my brother will take me.'

'Okay then, Good bye, I'll see you next week'

'Very good, Prynhawn da a diolch (good afternoon and thank you).'

I drove back to Tregaron and there were no more calls for me to attend to. I got back to the Talbot Hotel fairly early, Marjorie was having a rest so I made a few notes on what I had been doing that day. By about seven o'clock we were both ready for a meal. For some reason we were given a sumptuous dinner. I don't quite know why, but it started with fresh trout caught in the Teify river that day; the river runs through Tregaron. It was followed by roast pheasant, and blackcurrant tart to finish!

The next day at about nine o'clock my first call is at Rhydronnen to see any patients that have arrived to see the doctor. In the meantime we had a good night's sleep, undisturbed by calls!

Thursday morning
It's nine o'clock and I am in the front room again back at Rhydronnen in the square at Tregaron. I can hear the buzz of conversation coming from the shop. There is a knock on the door. I open it and there is a young boy with his small sister standing there.

'Hello, what can I do for you two?'

The boy looked about ten years old and he spoke up while his little sister tried to hide herself behind him.

'Mam says that Dada is not well and needs some medicine!'

'Come into the room. What is your name?'

'I am Trefor and this is my sister Enid.'

'Trefor what?' I ask. 'Jones' says he.

'What is your father called, Trefor?'

He looked puzzled. 'We call him Dada but,' and he giggled; 'Mam calls him...'

'Never mind what your Mam calls him, what's his first name?'

'David,' said he 'but they all call him Dai, or Dafydd.'

'Now Trefor, did your mother say what is the matter with your father?'

'He can't get up and he's rollin' around the bed in agony. He's been like this before and doctor gave him some white medicine that Mam says cured it.'

'Mam-gu (pronounced Mamgee) lives with us and she said we should ask the doctor to come to see him.'

'Your Granny is quite right,' I said. 'I'll call round as soon as I've finished here. Where do you live?'

Enid came suddenly to life. 'We live in Rose Cottage' she squeaked.

'Where is that, is it in Tregaron?'

'It's opposite Huw the chemist,' said Trefor.

'Please tell your mother that I'll call around as soon as I've finished here. Now you run home and tell your mother will you?'

Enid squeaked again. 'We've got to get the bread, and the milk, from the shop first, Mam said, not to forget.'

'Off you go then.' They ran back into the shop giggling.

The next patient was a middle aged lady dressed in working clothes and looking very well.

'Good morning,' I said. 'What can I do for you? I must say you look well enough.'

'Yes, it's not me, I want a note for the school for Evan.'

'Who is Evan?'

'He's my son, he's fifteen years old, and he's away from school.'

'D'you mean he's ill?' I asked.

She hesitates. 'Well yes, and the school has threatened me with the Attendance Officer. So I have to send in a sustificate.'

'Well, Mrs, er, what is the name?'

'Davies' she says.

'Mrs Davies,' say I, 'I cannot possibly give you a certificate to say that Evan is unfit to go to school through illness when I haven't even seen him.'

'Well I usually get one' says she, 'and it's a long way to bring him here to Tregaron'.

'Where do you live?' I ask.

'We are tenants of the Harrisons Estates and have the farm at Argoed.'

'Well, I am coming to Llangwyrfon this afternoon. What is the address at Argoed?'

'The farm is Tyn y Bwlch and we are right in the middle of the village.'

'I'll see you later on then, after dinner.'

I am thinking again about how I ended up here, and this is just the beginning. As Marjorie said, this is what I always wanted to do, but there's a long way to go. More hospital work to get more experience. I will have to take a House job in obstetrics and gynaecology. If I don't get that experience I won't be able to take on midwifery cases when I hopefully get into General Practice. Well actually, I am allowed, as things stand at the moment, to deal with any medical condition. But in fact it is expected in the medical profession that I would not undertake any procedure for which I had not got sufficient experience. So although I could attend patients in their confinement, I would not receive remuneration for this service in the NHS unless I had completed six months training in an obstetrics House appointment.

Tomorrow I have to see Hannah Watkins at Llanddewi and later I have to meet the gynaecologist at Llangwyryfon. I do hope that the uterine swelling isn't uterine cancer! As for Hannah: something is going on in her chest, hopefully nothing serious.

2

IN THE BEGINNING

I was born in Liverpool, in Priory Road Anfield on 20 March 1926, the year of the General Strike. The house my parents had rented was the normal residence of the Superintendent of Parks and Gardens and was in fact situated in the cemetery. I understand that from one of the upstairs windows there was a good view of Liverpool Football Ground. I don't remember it, of course. My family left Liverpool when I was just two years old. It was a very nice old house, I believe, but at that time it had not been connected to the supply of electricity; it was gas lit which I understand was not at all unusual even in towns at that time. My father had installed an ingenious system so that when you pushed a button by the door it forced air up a small copper pipe leading to the gas burner and operated a tap, hydraulically, that turned the gas light on which was lit by a pilot light which would be burning all the time. It all sounds very unsafe and dangerous by today's standards. I am quite sure that the arrangement wouldn't pass Health and Safety today! But I used to play with this little hydraulic switch, after it had been removed of course; so I remember that, at least.

It was rather a lonely house, or so it seemed to me when I visited it years later. One night Mother told me, that when my father was out at a meeting and she was alone in the house, there was a knock on the front door. She was nervous but she plucked up courage and opened the door. Outside stood a woman dressed all in black. She was clutching a bundle to her breast.

'Is Mr Godsef here?' the woman asked.

'This is no longer the office for Liverpool Parks and Gardens' replied mother.

'Please can you help me? I don't know what to do.'

Mother strained forward to look at the bundle the woman was carrying, but she turned away and started to weep.

'How can I help you, what are you carrying?'

The woman was sobbing. 'It's my baby' she said.

'Oh dear what is the matter with it, is it ill?'

'It's dead' she said. 'It was still-born.'

'I will telephone for help' said mother.

I understand that there was a telephone in the house because it had been Mr Godsef's office.

Mother told me that she 'phoned, I don't know to whom but the woman was led away with her stillborn baby, probably to Walton Hospital. I have been told this story several times, it evidently was an alarming experience.

My paternal grandfather, Nathan Smith (1842-1922).

When I was about two years old, we moved from Liverpool to Ipswich in East Anglia, my parents, my brother, Edward Hilary, and I. My parents found a house that they liked in Anglesea Road, number six. It had been occupied by the Governor of Ipswich Prison and his family, prior to his retirement. I do remember that house very fondly. It was detached and standing a little above the road. It had a big garden with a fig tree and inside, it had big white double doors into some of the downstairs rooms; very elegant. Apparently, Ipswich's big river, the Orwell, could be seen from the front windows upstairs. Father decided to call the house Riverena, but I am not sure that the name stuck after we had moved.

I don't know whether there were building societies in those days. I do not know whether my parents were able to purchase this house outright, but buy it they did. My father told me many years later that he had paid one thousand pounds for the property. He said that it had been put on the market at a higher price than that, but the price had been reduced

My paternal grandmother, Mary Elizabeth Smith (1841-1906).

for want of offers to buy; no doubt due to the recession that followed the First World War.

With respect to the hardship among poorer people that existed at that time, I remember seeing a group of about six men walking slowly and in step past the house singing, no doubt begging; a pathetic sight when one realises that these men were probably ex- service men who had fought for our country in the war which had ended only twelve years previously. I would not have realised at that time what these men were doing: but the maid we had at that time, Dorothy, and I were looking out of the window and she explained why they were doing this. The fact that I can remember this incident when aged no more than four means that even on my very young mind, it created an impression.

It was a happy sort of house to live in; the big garden with plenty of space for a child like me to play in and a new summer house.

When Father first joined the Board of Education, appointed to His Majesty's Inspectorate in 1922, he had been teaching at Appleby Grammar School. He was born in Halstead in Essex and educated at Colchester Grammar School. From there he had won a one year scholarship to study German Literature and Education at Jena University in Eastern Germany. I do not know how fluent his German speech was when he left the UK, but certainly he was fluent when he returned to England; I can remember hearing him talking, in the German language to a young man who briefly visited us from Switzerland when I was about seven years old.

When he returned to England he attended Birmingham University and there he studied Biology, Psychology and Education and was awarded a BA degree. I have his lecture notes and practical laboratory notes from that time; very colourful and beautifully drawn; but his description of the structure of protein was 'way out'– but that, was obviously the accepted view at that time. Later when living in Liverpool he received his MA degree, on the basis of a treatise on Education; not, the structure of protein it is to be hoped!

It was at Appleby School that my parents met each other. Mother had been brought up on a hill farm called Ffosybleiddied, in Cardiganshire; the name of the farm meaning the Last Ditch of the Wolf!

She was the eldest of four sisters. Her mother was, by all accounts an intelligent woman who, when she was young and before she was married, spent many hours sitting on the hillside caring for the sheep, shepherding: in Welsh *Bugeilio'r*. During these times, I am told she spent hours reading the Bible, so that as an adult she was well versed in the Holy Scriptures and no doubt she was very articulate. She probably received little more than Elementary School education herself, in the Welsh language, and would have left school aged twelve. She certainly could not speak much English, but she was a very determined woman and she said, I am told: 'I am going to see that my daughters receive a good education!'

The Welsh County Schools Act that created Secondary Grammar Schools in Aberystwyth, Towyn, Machynlleth, Aberayron and Tregaron had not come into effect at that time.

Grandmother said: 'If the new school at Tregaron is not opened in time for my children, they will attend the Ystrad Meurig School for Clergy. There is nothing in the deeds of that school that prohibits the admission of girls.'

The headmaster of that establishment at that time was known with some awe as Reverend John Latin Jones and he was, no doubt well aware of my grandmother's determined character. The theological college at Ystrad Meurig was, I understand, highly respected in this part of Cardiganshire. Most of its students went to Lampeter College to enter the church; but there existed closed scholarships from Ystrad Meurig to Jesus College Oxford and some of the more able young men ended up there reading theology in preparation for ordination as priests in the Church of England.

The disestablishment of the Church of Wales took place in 1914 following the Act of both Disestablishment and Disendowment of the Church in Wales. The Act was promoted by Lloyd George and fiercely opposed by the Conservative party, especially F. E. Smith, the famous barrister. Following the Act, the Church of Wales lost all its endowments which were distributed between the University of Wales and local authorities. Before the Disestablishment, all the Bishops in Wales had been English and this had caused great resentment in Wales.

'Take me to Jesus!' one young man said to the taxi driver on arriving at Oxford. 'Amen!' said the driver. How do these strange and unreal stories arise? There must be a nucleus of truth somewhere.

There was a strong affinity between Jesus College Oxford and this out of the way school in Ystrad Meurig, Cardighanshire. It is said that St John's College Ystrad Meurig challenged Jesus College Oxford to a contest, based on the classics. St John's College boasted an extraordinary headmaster who coached his pupils so well that they could dare to defy the might of Oxford. The Jesus team travelled down to somewhere near

Ffosybleiddied, 'The Last Ditch of the Wolf' home of my mother's family since the middle of the eighteenth century

Lampeter and then had to walk to Ystrad Meurig, a distance of some thirty miles. The wily headmaster, John Latin Jones, not only good at Latin, but possessing a crafty Welsh cunning, posted his best students on the road that he knew the Oxford team would travel. The Jesus contestants got a little lost on the way and stopped to ask a labourer on the road side the way to this remote village, Ystrad Meurig. They were, of course, answered in Latin by the student posing as a labourer. The story goes on… 'If the men working on the road are so proficient in the Classics, what hope have we got?' and they went back to Oxford!

The photograph on the following page is of the parish of Ystrad Meurig dated early in the twentieth century. I do not know what the

My grandmother, 'Mam-Gu', Jane Jones

occasion was, probably it was an anniversary to do with the school. They are dressed in their Sunday clothes. My grandmother Jane Jones (neé Williams) is sitting on the extreme left of the picture in the front row. John Latin Jones is just to the left of centre in the front. He is the gentleman with the large paunch and top hat. In the picture. He certainly looks a formidable character with a great paunch and a huge beard. My grandmother looks pretty determined too.

So Mother and her sister Bet attended the new Tregaron School, and did well enough to be admitted to the fairly new university at Aberystwyth, part of the University of Wales. They read Modern Languages, and both having been awarded a degree, they became school teachers. Mother's two other sisters remained in their home area. Annie married Thomas Charles Williams of Broncaradog, a yeoman farmer and Mal married Edward Ishmael who was a clergyman.

Mother and, believe it or not, her sister Bet, both ended up teaching at Appleby Grammar School, where they both met their husbands!

Just before the First World War started in 1914 my parents got married in Gwnnws church in the parish of Lledrod, mother's home parish. My grandfather, from Essex, on father's side came up to stay at Ffosybleiddied for the wedding and one Sunday evening he walked with father down to the village where a service was in progress at the Calvinistic Methodist Chapel. They stood outside listening to the minister preaching his sermon, in the Welsh language of course. In those days the minister would exhort his congregation not to sin, but to lead a pure sinless life; his voice rising as he rose to the climax of his sermon in a loud singing voice: that was called the *Hwyl*, or rising mood:

> And the people sinned; and the Lord struck them down. And they departed from the ways of God; and the Lord punished them. There was not one of them pure and they were castigated because they were sinners. And how many of you my friends are sinners to be struck down?
>
> And they went on board the ship of life, but their lives were sinful. Their ship sank because it had a hole in its bottom. And how many of you my friends...

'Do you think the good Lord can understand them?' asked my grandfather.

Father was aged 31 then, at the start of the war; too old to be conscripted, but later as the war dragged on more and more older men were conscripted into the armed forces. My father, possibly fearing conscription into the war, that was killing millions of men, and knowing full well

Battlebarrow, Appleby, circa 1910.

Appleby Grammar School circa 1910 (?). Father and mother third and fourth from left. Gillian Counsel, the headmaster's daughter standing by Mother.

that he would make a very poor soldier, joined the work force of the armaments factory at Workington and stayed there making artillery shells until the end of the war. I feel sure he was more useful there.

When Armistice was declared in 1918 father returned to teach at Appleby. Here he was to realise one of his lifelong ambitions: to make electric light.

As a boy in Halstead he had heard of the use of electricity for house lighting. The owners of some of the larger houses in England owned by wealthy people had installed a generator to light their homes. Most people at that time understood very little about the nature and use of electric power. For some reason, father was obsessed with the idea of trying to make electric light. It would be years later when teaching at Appleby before he was able to fulfil his wish.

I imagine that he had read about Faraday's experiments and demonstrations of the power of electricity – incidentally Faraday's family came from Mallerstang at the top of the Eden Valley.   Father knew, he told me that he had to pass an electric current through a wire, in sufficient quantity to make the wire hot; to glow perhaps. He had no source of electricity. The only battery that he knew of was the Leclanché cell, forerunner of the modern dry battery invented by George Leclanché in 1866 less than twenty years before father was born; so it was very new, and was, he knew, used almost entirely to work a domestic bell system that takes very little electric current.

Like our modern dry battery the Leclanché produces 1.5 volts; not enough he knew to make a thin wire glow. So he tried joining several of these batteries together to try to produce more power. Unfortunately, when a number of these batteries are joined together in series, although the voltage does increase, the internal electric resistance also increases in proportion, so that the heating power of the system does not increase correspondingly. Also of course, even if he had managed to make a thin wire glow it would have oxidised and melted very quickly; as demonstrated by Edison in America and Swan in England who filled their light bulbs with an inert gas thereby allowing the filament to glow without oxidising and melting. So all Father's efforts as a boy would have been in vain!

He was not to be deterred. At the end of the war in 1918, having left the munitions factory in Workington, he returned to Appleby and took up his former post teaching boys several subjects that included, not only mathematics and English, but practical subjects like metal work, engineering practises and electricity that he had learned much about during his work in the factory at Workington. So he started a project with some of the senior boys who joined in very enthusiastically, to construct a windmill to drive a dynamo to make electric light.

He purchased a redundant hut and a quantity of tools and equipment that had been used at the Workington site and now sold off cheaply. He set up a workshop and he and the boys built a windmill about 25 feet tall. The rotor had multiple sails similar to the windmills that can still be seen pumping water in remote rural areas in this country and abroad. The mill drove a dynamo that produced twelve volts and lit small lamps in one or two rooms in the school. I know very little of the details. They must have had storage batteries, if not, the light would only shine when the wind blew! But it was the first electric light in Appleby I am told. I have photographs of the windmill tower being erected by him and the boys.

These are the boys with my father who erected the windmill, most of the materials were 'war surplus' materials, left over at the end of the 1914 to 1918 war.

During this very happy time for my parents, they lived in Slapestone House, near the Sands and only a quarter of a mile from the school. The back of the house is adjacent to the path that runs along the river Eden and father told me he had many happy hours fishing in that river. It was a pleasant time for them both I believe and they led a full social life. Mother being a   married woman had to give up teaching but took on several private pupils. The school at that time was for boys only. So Mother's pupils were young girls from the town whose parents, evidently like my grandmother wanted their girls to be educated; and so they were, privately at home.

At the end of the war two new members of staff were appointed: Mother's sister Bet, teaching French and Latin, and John Minchin from County Sligo in the Republic of Ireland. He had served throughout the war as a captain in the Artillery and was lucky enough to have survived with no injuries. He taught mathematics and was by all accounts a very good teacher, especially for pupils who had difficulty with mathematics. I know, because I was such a one and he was excellent at explaining difficult concepts.

Here is the windmill before and after erection with part of Appleby Grammar School in the background.

He and my aunt Bet were married in the late 1920s and bought their house at Bongate in Appleby. They continued teaching at Appleby Grammar School until retirement. I believe they had a very happy life during their time at Appleby. Both were very keen golfers and bridge players and they took part in the full social life of Appleby town. John Minchin died in Appleby in the 1950s, and when that happened Bet moved to Aberystwyth to be near to my parents who were then living at Hafod House, Ystrad Meurig. My parents' move to Liverpool just about coincided with the appointment of my aunt and John Minchin to the school teaching staff.

To return to the time Father and Mother lived in Liverpool. My parents moved from the peaceful county town of Appleby with its vibrant social life to a new and different life in the big city. I believe that when Father was appointed as HMI, his first year or two would have been working with a more senior member of the inspectorate. His district in the city was in the area all around the centre: Walton Road, Edge Hill, Old Swan and all the areas around the centre of the city. He did not need a car to take him to the schools he had to visit; I assume that there were

various forms of public transport available. Certainly the installation of the trams had been going on for some years. In 1897, the Liverpool Corporation bought The United Tramway and Omnibus Company and an Act of Parliament in the same year enabled Liverpool Corporation to start installing the service that actually began operation in 1898. The first electric tram left Dingle in Liverpool in November 1898. So Father was able to get around the city without the use of a car.

Apart from inspecting the accommodation in the various schools to approve or recommend new building, sanitary arrangements, lighting, etc., and the general fitness for purpose of a school building, probably the most important part of his job was to see that the children were being taught properly and encouraged in the good use of the English language, and that included handwriting.

The senior HM inspector to whom Father was attached in his work was a rather stern and formidable man, a Mr John Charles. On one occasion Mr Charles visited a small elementary school near Walton Hall Drive. There was one teacher, a young and rather timid lady who opened the door when he arrived. She was breathless, flustered and blushing. 'Good morning' greeted the inspector: 'My name is Charles!'

'Oh' exclaimed the young lady, 'mine is Gladys, do come in.'

A student investigating electric circuits.

I am not sure how much my father liked the job of being a school inspector, with all the administration that was involved. I know that his heart was really in teaching. He was very aware of the fact that at that time, practically no science was being taught in elementary schools. Certainly nature study and possibly some elements of simple chemistry may have been included, but the relatively new subject of electricity and magnetism was not on the syllabus. He

Slapestone House, Battlebarrow, showing the Slapestones

felt that some knowledge of the use and properties of electricity that was being increasingly used in and about the home should be part of a school child's education. Small lamps powered by dry batteries were replacing candle and paraffin lanterns for use out of doors and battery powered bicycle lights were being used instead of acetylene lamps in which water was added to calcium carbide to produce an inflammable gas that lit a flame to give light. Electric bells and telephones were making their appearance in the home.

There was also an increasing element of danger from accidental contact with live electricity wires. Today it is taken for granted that any appliance in which the casing is metal, has to be earthed. Nearly all electric plugs have three pins, one of which is the earth pin. In my childhood, the commonest electric appliance apart from electric light, was the electric smoothing iron. This was nearly always plugged into the light socket via a 'double fitting', with the electric flex trailing down to the iron on the table. The concept of the electric cable with three wires: live, neutral and earth was not in evidence much.

Electric power in towns and cities was produced by local power stations and the voltage could vary from town to town. Appliances would have to be suited to the different local supplies, mostly, either 110 or 230 volts. There were warning notices on new electric products telling the purchaser to check that the appliance voltage suited the supply voltage where it was to be used. Some electric points still give the option of 110 or 230 volts for electric shavers and other similar items.

The great move forward was the establishment of the Electric Grid System in the 1930s when all electric power was at a standard voltage throughout the country. Electricity had to be transported over long distances and this would have inevitably resulted in a loss of power; so that if a power station produced electricity at 230 volts and transmitted it over many miles, the voltage would drop significantly. Also the cables carrying the power would have to be very thick to carry the huge currents making the whole project very cumbersome and expensive.

All this was overcome by the use of alternating current that could easily be 'stepped up' by transformers to very high voltages and carried on the electric pylons that we see all over the country today. These, as everyone knows, carry current at huge voltages; in the region of 240,000 volts. Now the power in watts is a product of the volts multiplied by the amps, so if the volts are very high, the current, or heating power will be low to arrive at the same power. By this means, current was taken across country long distances avoiding huge losses of power. In the local areas the electricity was 'stepped down' by the transformer to the correct supply voltage for use in the home. This is taken for granted today; but in the 1930s most people did not understand the concept of an electric circuit; of how electricity produced by a power source could be arranged in an electrical circuit and harnessed safely to operate electric appliances.

It was for this reason that Father invented the teaching aid designed to help children in school understand the elements of   electricity. It was a simple black board perforated regularly with holes into which small components such as switches, lamps, coils and bells could be plugged and all connected up with bright metal strips to complete a circuit that would be energised with a battery making a working model. He introduced this simple apparatus into schools and showed teachers how they could build it themselves. When this was set up in front of a class, the

Dining room at Slapestone House before the First World War.

black board and bright metal strips provided a very clear picture of the nature of an electric circuit. The pupils themselves together with the teacher could set up the demonstration, like building a model in Meccano. A battery could be attached and the model electric bell, motor, telephone or other device could be seen clearly to work. He called the apparatus Electrano. The then Chief Inspector of Schools, Sir Graham Savage called the apparatus the 'Live Blackboard'.

In those days, the Board of Education held science courses for teachers in an attempt to encourage good ideas in science teaching. Father used to attend and help on these summer courses. He showed the teachers attending the course how they could build the apparatus and provided those who were interested with some of the necessary materials. By the 1940s his Electrano included model transformers and all the experiments that went with low voltage alternating current: the synchronous motor which was the motor used in electric clocks that kept such good time, a demonstration of induction heating, the latest thing today on the domestic cooker, electric welding and many other experiments relative to modern electric appliances. He would have liked to have marketed Electrano, but as a government employee, he was not allowed to do so.

When he retired from the then Ministry of Education he set up the supply firm that he named Electrano Scientific Instruments Ltd. It was a very successful post-retirement venture and I having at that time a great deal of spare time, being at the end of my first year of medical studies was able to help.

When my parents had moved to Ipswich, I was only two years old. For some reason they did not send me to school until I was seven! They then sent me to a queer little 'Dame School' called Miss Morris's. It was held in a building rather like a village hall: one big room and furnished with the usual desks for the pupils – all boys, and a blackboard. I can remember very little about it. Miss Morris was a plump uninspiring woman who ruled the class with a ruler applied to the hand of a pupil for misbehaviour.

Our lessons consisted of reading, writing, arithmetic and copy book writing. In the latter, we were given a note book with writing in neat copper plate printed on one line and we were supposed to copy it on the line below. We used pen holders with steel nibs, and the ink was made up from a powder mixed with water. The ink wells on the desks were refilled with this every morning. The ink was very likely to drop off the nib on to your work making a blotty mess. I was useless at this and my writing today shows how useless the exercise of copy writing was. We also had a great deal of dictation in which I produced multiple spelling mistakes and blots!

My family left Ipswich when I was eight years old and we moved to South Croydon. I attended a prep school called Wood Vale House. This school was supposed to prepare its pupils for the Common Entrance exam for admission to the Public School system. I must say that I learned a lot of Latin but very little else. I was indeed a poor scholar in a school environment with which I was out of tune.

When I reached the age of ten plus, I sat the entrance examination to obtain admission to Whitgift School. The Whitgift Foundation was very old, going back to the reign of Queen Elizabeth the First. I remember there were two other school buildings other than the modern one that I attended with the name of Whitgift. One was in East Croydon and called Whitgift Middle which I think was not an independent fee paying school. I was told that the other building with that name was a 'Home for Incurables!' It is now, according to Wikipedia, a girls' school – not a very encouraging name to attract prospective parents if it is true.

When one alters a name or a title, it can produce comic results, like the Liverpool football fan who had tattooed on his leg, 'You'll Never Walk Alone'. In the recent Afghan War, he was injured and part of his leg was amputated. The tattoo tragically now reads 'You'll never walk.'

Whitgift School now has a brilliant reputation for academic success, but I didn't like school, so I never benefited from what it had to offer. There were however two incidents during my time there that were worth noting.

The first happened in October 1937. There was an outbreak of typhoid fever in Croydon. There were 297 cases and 43 patients died. Everyone was scared, and we all boiled our drinking water. In the middle of this scare, one day I was standing in the school hall for morning assembly when the hall seemed to be spinning and I fell to the ground in a faint. I had, up to that point, never enjoyed so much kind attention from the school, whose regime was generally harsh. I was carried down by one of the teachers to his car, I think it was H. A. C. Evans – known as Hac. He was Welsh and from Brecon. Mother knew him, she usually managed to find anyone in her circle who was Welsh! I was taken home in style and put to bed. The doctor was called. Dr Cutlack lived next door to us and I really liked him, especially when he confirmed that I had not caught typhoid and ordered a week off school.

The next incident however was not at all pleasant. In April of 1938 my cousin David who was at school in Brecon came to visit us. We were taken to see the sights of London. We visited the usual places of interest: David had never been to London or, for that matter, into England before. We stood outside the Houses of Parliament, being told we could not enter at that time, when a man came up to us and said 'I know that badge, it's Whitgift isn't it?' He was looking at my brother Hilary's blazer. 'I am Herbert Williams, your Member of Parliament.' He took us around all the important places in the Commons explaining everything to us; even the dent in the door where Black Rod strikes it.

Two days after that day in London I became ill. Dr Cutlack diagnosed scarlet fever. This disease is caused by the haemolytic streptococcus. This bug is powerful: it settles in the throat, produces toxins and it can be fatal, especially in children. The germ is sensitive to penicillin the use of which nowadays cures the disease when it occurs; so it does not occur very often today and when it does strike it is a much milder disease.

There was no penicillin when I was eleven years old. So Dr Cutlack ordered my immediate admission to the fever hospital.

'You cannot leave this child at home,' he said. 'The other two children will catch the disease.'

So off I went; I was barely conscious of what was happening. I spent nine weeks in that hospital. I can remember very little of what went on in the first few weeks. Mother had said she would visit me and for the first few days, I remember asking when she was coming. Then, I imagine, I was so feverish and ill that I stopped asking. In fact visitors were not allowed because of spreading the infection. Knowing what I know now, I believe that I was very near death then. It was all like a dream or a nightmare. I can remember the feeling, even now.

The next event that I recall was waking up one morning and seeing my brother in the next bed. He had become ill some three or four weeks after me. Dr Cutlack on being called again had said to mother: 'It is impossible for Hilary to have caught it from Brian. The incubation period is just two days.'

Mother said: 'I am sure I am not mistaken; having seen one of my children with this rash admitted to hospital, I am sure that Hilary's rash is the same!'

The riddle was eventually solved. Hilary did indeed have scarlet fever and he had caught it from David, not from me. In the last days of David's term at Brecon school he had complained of a sore throat. A swab had been taken which confirmed that he was a carrier of the disease. A person can carry some diseases without actually suffering the effects of it. I really cannot understand, now why he was allowed out to mix with other children when the disease was such a serious one.

My memories of the hospital remind me of *Oliver Twist*. For the first few days I was fed on sweet soggy bread and milk. They insisted on sweetening the concoction which made it very sickly and they totally refused to put salt in instead of sugar. Later when I was better, at tea time we had jam sandwiches, just two; no more. When at last my appetite started to return, one day, like Oliver, I asked for more; another sandwich. No was the answer – I was hungry, damn it! At this stage I was beginning to recover.

One afternoon a very large, august, and imposing lady came around the ward. She was followed by a retinue of nurses and the ward sister, all were looking tense and frightened. This was the hospital matron and she was dressed very regally with a large wimple covering her head that made her even more imposing. She looked closely at me, a thin little waif and said in a commanding upper class tone: 'Why is he so thin?'

The nurses shuffled and failed to reply.

'What would you like for tea?' she asked me. Really the first kind voice I had heard since leaving home. Was this an angel come to save me from starvation?' I asked myself.

'Please, I would like some strawberry jam sandwiches' said I. And this is the punch line, or was, for me at that time: 'He is to have as many strawberry jam sandwiches as he wants,' said she in a commanding tone. The nurses looked shocked, but they had to obey.

There was a very strict barrier between the hospital and the outside world, so that when Hilary and I were deemed to have recovered and to be fit enough to be discharged, we had to be taken to a building some way away from the ward. This was called Block Two, the intermediate place between hospital and home and was talked about with some awe by us boys. There were three of us in the small ward there, and we had to remain enclosed with no access to the outside world for three days: quarantine. A doctor came immediately we arrived and took swabs from the throat and looked into our ears to make sure that we were not carrying the infection out of the hospital. It was peaceful there in Block Two. All was very quiet and no longer could we hear the plaintiff call: 'Nurse, Nurse, I want a bottle.' That had gone on all day and all night in the wards. We had a bathroom and toilet now; getting back to normal. At the end of the third day, Hilary and I were bundled into an ambulance and taken home.

After my long stay of nine weeks in the hospital most of which I was a bed patient, not even getting up to the toilet, but having to use a bed pan; it was not surprising that I was only barely able to walk. Mother had to arrange for a young lady called Marion, who was training to be a masseuse; nowadays called a physiotherapist, to come and give me exercises.

After I had quite recovered, we all went to stay in a bungalow by the sea at Selsea. I know it was very kind of the owner to let us have the bungalow but in truth I was bored stiff. The bonus was that I didn't have to go back to school that term. Instead I looked forward with keen anticipation to our next holiday: 1938 summer holiday.

The year of 1938 was, as some people remember, the time when Europe held its breath. The time when the Nazis had gained power and seemed to be threatening all of Western Europe, and we in Britain feared that once again we were going to be drawn into a European war. It was the time when Neville Chamberlain returned to Britain waving a piece of paper that he told us was an agreement with Adolf Hitler that Austria was the last of Germany's territorial claims. 'Peace in our time', said our Prime Minister. I was twelve years old, but I can remember feeling that the knot in Europe was tightening. I had no idea at that time in my life of what implications war would bring, but I do remember that it was a time that we called 'The Crisis'. We all went home from Wales, and I back to school. Our newspaper headline stated at the time, "Have no fear, there will be no war!'

How wrong they were. I returned to school to see some air raid shelters being dug in the school grounds. I think many people believed that in the event of a war, the first thing that would happen would be an air raid. But life went on as normal, and once again as spring processed into summer, it was time to think about summer holidays. Once again, we, as a family went to the place I thought of as heaven on earth – Wales.

In July 1938 we set off for Wales. This was always, every year, the highlight of my life. A whole month living in the cottage called Trefriwfach that had been my grandfather's home in his retirement from farming. He had died two years before, and we had kept the cottage on for our summer holidays. I cannot exaggerate my happiness when on holiday there. Our cottage was just 200 yards from the farm owned by my Uncle Tom and Auntie Annie – Mother's sister. I was never bored and I loved being in contact with all that went on there, and in the countryside around. However, all good things often come to an end, and I did not look forward to our return to Croydon and Whitgift School.

3

TREGARON

Time goes by very quickly indeed when you are on call day and night in a country practice. You cannot really let up your guard for a moment. In spite of my friend Sam's reassuring advice I had fears that at any time day or night I could be called to a patient with some life threatening condition in which I was expected to take immediate action to save the situation. It is not at all like working in a hospital, where senior colleagues are on call to advise and reassure at all times. I did not feel this anxiety so much in the day time, but on a dark night or in the early hours I did feel some trepidation sometimes.

There is another worry, just at night, that of being able to find the house to which I have been called. There is no problem in the day time because there is always someone around to give helpful directions. But on one occasion I was called in the early hours of the morning to a patient whom, I was told was gravely ill and I was given just the name of the house and the district in a sparsely populated country area in Lincolnshire. At the time I had only just started work there. It was my first assistantship in a country practice.

'What is the address?' I asked.

'Rose Cottage' the caller replied.

'Yes, but where is that exactly?'

'Oh it's 'agin' the Hare and Hounds. D'ye know where that is?'

I did recognise the site of the pub, and that is where I went only to find two or three fields on each side of the hostel and no sign of a dwelling. So I searched about half a mile up and down the isolated road and eventually located Rose Cottage. At that time of night there are no lights in the houses of folk who might give helpful directions… 'agin' the Hare and Hounds' indeed!

Patients in country areas are mostly considerate and understanding in this respect and will often leave a light showing to guide the doctor who may be unfamiliar with the area.

I had undertaken to look after Dr Alun's practice while he was on holiday in London. Everything went well in that ten days as it happened. Luck was clearly on my side and I did not encounter any acute night time problems that I did not feel quite adequate to deal with. I must confess that on one or two occasions when driving down an unlit country road in the early hours of the morning to see an emergency, the nature of which had been made clear by the caller was serious, I prayed silently to my old experienced GP to guide me!

The reader may quite justifiably ask, 'What the hell was I, 'green at the gills' as it were, doing, undertaking such work that would normally be done by an experienced medic?' Well it may be of some comfort to know that today, all young doctors who want to work as General Practitioners have to undertake a period of training under a recognised 'trainer doctor' that is a GP who has been approved to teach young doctors how to manage and cope with the various problems that arise in General Practice; in addition to this, the budding GP will have completed a period as a very junior hospital doctor in most cases.

When I qualified as a doctor none of this was obligatory. Quite often young doctors fresh from the final exams and newly registered by the General Medical Council would be employed as *locum tenens* in General Practice for short holiday periods while they looked around to decide what they wanted to do in life. The practise of medicine as a GP was much simpler then.

It was Thursday morning and my first call was to David Jones in Rose Cottage. This was a terraced cottage opposite the chemist just as the children told me. The door was open, I knocked and called out: 'It's the doctor, anyone at home?' There was a scampering down the stairs and little Enid shouted: 'Trefor, Trefor, the doctor's here, where's Mam?'

Trefor came running: 'She's gone across to the chemist to get Dada some more of that medicine.'

'Trefor,' I said, 'will you just run across and tell her not to buy the medicine, and that I am here. I will see to it.'

Mrs Jones came hurrying back across the road, breathless.

'So sorry doctor, I had to do something, Dafydd was groaning with the pain. I'm so glad you're here. Come upstairs he's in bed, he's had a terrible night.'

David was lying on his back clutching his stomach.

'Hullo Mr Jones, I'm Dr Frost-Smith. I'm standing in for Dr Alun. I understand you're having a lot of pain in your stomach. Could you please lie flat and show me where the pain is.'

He pointed to his epigastrium just below the breast bone or sternum.

'Let me have a look at you.' He was pale and a little drawn and his tongue was heavily coated. I put my hand on his abdomen and he jumped.

'Ow that's cold!' I warmed my hands on the hot water bottle in his bed and tried again.

'Try to relax,' I said. His abdomen was soft; no rigidity. 'Show me where the pain is worst.' He pointed again to his solar plexus.

'Does the pain go down your arm?'

'No it's always just there and I bring up acid into my mouth. The pain seems better if I drink milk, and that medicine Dr Alun gave me eases it, only I've finished the bottle he gave me.'

Today's teaching is: 'A bad pain in the chest is a heart attack until proved otherwise.' Today, there are all sorts of tests, blood tests and electronic tests that help a doctor to make a firm diagnosis. None of these were easily available in a remote country practice at the time I am writing about. The doctor just had to make a judgement based on clinical signs and symptoms.

'I think you have a stomach ulcer; probably a duodenal ulcer. and it's caused by your stomach producing too much acid. You'll have to get it seen to; it'll give you no peace if you don't. I'll send you to a specialist and he'll investigate to see what is going on in that stomach of yours. In the meantime I'll give you some more medicine.' I wrote a prescription for mist bismuth et mag hydroxide. 'Take this three times a day at meal times, and you'll have to be careful with your diet. I'll have a chat with your wife about that.'

'Yes, you tell Meg what I'm to eat. She's a smashing cook, and she'll see to it.'

'What sort of treatment will the specialist recommend do you think?' he asked.

'Well, I think he may suggest an operation in which they remove the part of your stomach that is producing too much acid.'

'And will that cure it?'

'It's the best treatment that we have at present, but I think it would be best to discuss it with the specialist.'

'I will write a letter and ask for an appointment. The hospital will let you know when to go, and if you have any problem, you must let me or Dr Alun know.'

The operation of partial gastrectomy was the only treatment at the time, apart from supportive treatments like diet and various alkali medicines. Gastrectomy was radical and not always successful. There were long term problems and surgeons were reluctant to do it unless all other conservative treatment had failed. When a large part of the stomach was removed, the part that produced the intrinsic factor for the production of Vitamin B12 was reduced as well as the acid bearing part, and that could lead to abnormalities in the patient's blood.

Unfortunately drinking antacids did not solve the problem. As fast as the stomach acids were neutralised by the medicine, the brain simply sent a message to the stomach to produce more!

The solution came in the 1970s. Drugs that inhibited the production of acid centrally from the brain. I think Tagamet was one of the first and it revolutionised the treatment of this painful complaint – more and better ones have followed.

I left Dafydd feeling a little anxious and had a brief talk with Meg about diet, explaining how spicy foods and condiments like pepper and mustard would stimulate stomach acid production. I was concerned, the poor man was in distress. I said I would call in a day or two to see how he was getting on. Before I left I gave him 50 mg of pethidine by injection to ease the pain, because it was so severe.

I was quite confident that his ulcer had not perforated through the wall of the stomach. I had also eliminated other commoner causes of acute abdominal pain. Dr Baker Bates, a prominent medical consultant and a great teacher, used to tell his students: 'if you see a bird in the garden, it's probably a sparrow not a canary.' That means that David's abdominal pain is most likely to be one of the commoner emergency conditions. I would not be looking for a diagnosis of something rare. I explained the situation in detail to Meg.

'I'll come back to see him tomorrow. I have to be in Llangwyryfon by eleven thirty, so it will be before that.'

I drove back into the town and out on the road to Llanddewi Brefi where Hannah Watkins lived. It is a pretty little village and has some connection with my mother. When Mother was a pupil at Tregaron school, she had a very close friend who was the daughter of the Minister of the local church. They always sat together in class and tended to compete with each other.

They both studied modern language and both were admitted to the University of Wales at Aberystwyth. They shared a room together at the women's hostel, Alexandra Hall and both took their degree of BA at the same time, but at that point they each went their own way; both into teaching.

At that time there was a rigid policy of segregation in Aber' Coll' as it was called. No, not black and white, but male and female! Men students when within the college, did not speak to women students. In the centre of the old college building by the sea is a large quadrangular hall, called 'The Quad'. Between lectures students used to parade up and down this hall, men on one side and women on the other. If a student wished to talk to a member of the opposite sex, he or she would have to cross over to the other side in full view of everyone and talk openly! That is how it was in mother's time – 1903 to 1907. Not much chance of male–female fraternisation!

Even in my day, in 1943 at Aberystwyth the women students were kept strictly in check. Even if they were living in private lodgings, or 'digs' a watch was kept on their comings and goings especially at night. I believe they had to sign in and sign out, with permission of course.

In mother's time there, in Alexander Hall, the ladies had to behave with decorum and there were maids who waited on them, serving their meals etc. I still have the dainty tea set that mother and her friend would use to entertain a visitor in hall. We as a family kept in close touch for many years with mother's friend and her family. I have made contact with one of her family recently, a doctor in London, though I have never actually met her.

So I arrived in the village and it wasn't difficult to find Bryn yr Afon where Hannah lived. It was a small stone built cottage in the centre, near the non-conformist church. I knocked and went in and was met by a woman who looked like Hannah but perhaps a little older.

'Good morning doctor,' said she, 'you are the doctor who's come to see my sister are you? You look too young to be a doctor!'

'Yes, I am standing in for Dr Alun while he is away.'

'I am Blodwen, please come upstairs to see my sister.'

This rather personal remark about my looking too young, happened to me a lot in my early years as a GP. I didn't mind, but later in my life, I took on a recently qualified young man in my practice who had just completed his training to be a GP and he looked young, as I had looked at that stage. After some months had passed and when I returned from my holiday and saw him for the first time in two weeks, I hardly recognised him, he had grown a beard!

'I had to grow it,' he said, 'all the patients kept telling me that I looked too young to be a doctor, and I got fed up with it. I thought it was taking away their confidence in me.' In a year's time he shaved it off, feeling more sure of himself.

In the bed room Hannah was propped up in bed.

'Good morning doctor, I'm all ready and waiting.'

'Would you like me to go?' asked Blodwen.

'No, will you please stay and help your sister if she needs you.'

'Now then, you'll need to take your top off so I can examine your chest.'

'She's been coughing all night,' said Blodwen 'I could hear her.'

I haven't worked in hospital for over sixty years, so I am not at all sure just what sort of initial examination a junior hospital doctor will carry out on a new patient, who has been admitted with a chest infection. I suspect that a chest X ray will be one of the first tests to be carried out.

We, as students fell under the stern and severe teaching of our professor of medicine, Prof. Jock Kennedy. We were shown how to examine a patient's chest and we were expected to carry out an examination using our touch, sight, and listening senses. If you felt and listened carefully you were expected to be able to isolate a small area of consolidation in the lung due perhaps to a patch of pneumonia. These days, an X ray delivers an instant and exact diagnosis; always assuming that an X ray machine is available.

In 1934, King George V had a bad illness, with fever, chest pain and exhaustion. The doctors were divided. Some said he had pneumonia, the old man's friend as it was called; but others thought he had some fluid in the pleural cavity – a pleural effusion or empyema, if the fluid is pus – in the area between the lung and the chest wall. The old man was desperately ill. In a desperate attempt to solve the problem, an X ray machine was brought into Buckingham Palace into the King's bedroom and his chest X rayed. This was a new excursion into medical diagnosis, X rays were first discovered by Wilhelm Rontgen in Germany at the end of the nineteenth century. He was awarded the first Nobel Prize.

The X ray clearly showed a pleural effusion or possibly an empyema. It was drained and the King recovered. 'Dangerous Corner' Mrs Simpson had not appeared at that point. If X rays had not been used, it is quite likely that the King would have died. Then Edward, Prince of Wales would have been crowned king!

I examined Hannah's chest as I was taught. There was no pneumonia but she had moist sounds at the bases of both lungs, crepitations or creps as they are called. This means that she has an infection and needs Penicillin or an antibacterial drug. Her temperature had gone up to just under 100 degrees F. I wrote a prescription for sulphapyridine, the M and B 693 that I had been given ten years previously!

'I will come and see you tomorrow Hannah. Huw Evans will send you these tablet on the bus this afternoon.'

'You must take one tablet four times a day. If they make you vomit you must let me know.'

I drove back to Tregaron at lunch time, but on the way I called in to see Miss Davies to see if there were any other messages.

'Yes' she said, 'there are two. Will you call and see Jacob Owen, he lives in a farm up on the Abergwesyn road. It's the second farm on the right, about half a mile from Tregaron Square. It's called Penderlwn Goch.'

'Did he say what was the matter?' I asked. 'Yes He fell and has hurt his back.'

'What's the second call?' I asked. 'Oh it's little Jennie Hopkins of 5 New Row. They are both on the same Abergwesyn road but – New Row is just out of the town. It's a row of new houses on the left, just after you leave the square.' I planned to do these two calls in the afternoon after I'd been to Llangwyryfon.

Marjorie had been for a walk and done a few more rows of knitting. 'What's it going to be when it's finished?'

'Can't you tell?'

'Well it looks like the start of a pair of pants.'

'You know nothing,' she said with a smile. 'They're pilches, that's the name your mother called them: baby's woollen pants worn over the nappy. Lovely and warm and made out of Welsh wool that does not shrink when it is washed.'

'OK let's have some lunch. What are you having? I'm going for the cawl again if it's on.'

'Well, I'm having toasted sandwiches again, they were delicious.'

After lunch Marjorie went to lie down for a rest and I set off to go to Llangwyryfon to see Evan Davies at Tan y Bwlch. I would have to do the two new calls when I got back to Tregaron.

There were three patients waiting for me at the farm: Tyn yr Afon. The first was a young lady who had come for an antenatal check up. She was six months pregnant with her second pregnancy. I checked her blood pressure and did a urine check. All was well and abdominally; a vertex (head) presentation. She was feeling movements.

'Where are you having the baby?' I asked.

'I'm havin' it at home. The midwife has been to see me and she says my house is quite OK to have the baby in. I've a son too and he's very anxious for the baby to come, he's quite excited; so are we all really.' She laughed.

'Have you got a family, doctor?'

She looked at me: 'No, you're too young I think.' Here we go again I thought.

'My wife is expecting our first, in February' I said.

'But now, could you come back for another check up in a fortnight, and don't be doing too much hard work?'

The next patient was a young lad with a painful wrist.

'How did you do that?' I asked.

'Turnin' cartwheels in the playground. I must have put too much strain on my hand. They took me to Old Weedy, and he said I had to come and see you. "Don't let me catch you doing it again" he had said. But I had to, as a dare, just as he was coming into the yard and he gave me a clip around my ear'ole. I didn't mind, he's OK really.'

'Who,' I asked 'is Old Weedy?'

'He's our headmaster, Mr W. D. Iddon.'

I looked at his wrist. It was swollen, but there was no tenderness and he had full movement. 'I don't think it's broken, I'll put a crepe bandage on it and no more cartwheels in the school yard. You get you mother to bring you back if it isn't better in a few days.'

'OK, pob hwyl (good luck)' said he and away he went.

I drove to Argoed village. The farm Tyn y Bwlch was, as Mrs Evans had said, right in the centre. I looked at the front door; Some climber was growing over it, I think it was ivy. It looked as if it hadn't been used for some time. I didn't bother to try that way in. I went round into the yard and found Mrs Evans feeding the pigs.

'Good afternoon,' I called. 'I've come to see Evan, like I said.'

'Oh Du Du he's not here!'

'Well, you were expecting me, weren't you?' I asked.

'Oh sorry, Ei fod yn y cae. O dear sorry again you don't speak Welsh do you?'

'Not much I must admit, but I understand it mostly.'

'He's in the field, that's what you're telling me. Well what's he doing in the field? You said he is too ill to go to school.'

'I'll have to explain. This is the time of year when the potatoes have to be picked and sorted. Like the corn and hay harvest it is a very important time. We have to get extra help to get the job done quickly. So our neighbour comes to give a hand and then we do the same for him. You may not understand, having lived in the town, how difficult it is for upland farmers in Wales to make a living.'

'Oh no' I said ' I spent most of my life in a village near Ystrad Meurig, and our house is on my uncle's farm, Broncaradog. So I am quite familiar with farm life you see.'

'Oh I know the Williams of Broncaradog. I'm sure you'll understand now, if that's where you come from.'

'Evan is fifteen. He doesn't really like school, well to be honest he's not very interested in what goes on there. So you see he'll be leaving school next July when he's sixteen, and he can't wait to start here, farming. That is all he wants to do. Having been brought up to help his Dad, he's never happier than when he's out in the fields. He came second in a ploughing competition last year. He handles the horses well, and he sings or whistles to them. It's slow work, but he finds it very satisfying to plough a straight furrow. Some of the farmers down in the valley have a tractor, but we still use Welsh Cobs.'

'Now,' I said 'you'd better go and fetch him so I can see him, because although I understand what you're telling me, it doesn't alter the fact that I won't give a certificate unless I've seen the patient and am satisfied that what I'm saying is true.'

'I won't be a minute, I'll run down to yr Cae Hir (the Long Field).'

'Now Efan' I said when he appeared, breathless through running to the house. 'How are you'?

'I'm not too bad' said he with a grin. 'But I want to finish picking the tatws (potatoes). I think I was a bit run down yesterday, and today I seemed to be a bit slow.'

I looked at his conjunctivae. He was a bit pale.

'OK 'I said I'll give your mother a prescription for a tonic for you and I'll write a note for the school suggesting that you stay at home for a week or so until you feel better. What do you do in your spare time?' I asked.

'You mean when I'm not chasing the girls,' said he with a grin.

'Now Evan, behave yourself,' said his mother.

'I like reading as a matter of fact.'

'What are you reading just now.'

'It's a book called *A Welsh Country Upbringing*.'

'Right, you go back to help your father now'

'Diolch yn fawr (Thank you very much) doctor. I'd better get back to dad.'

I got back to Tregaron and it was only three o'clock. So I went straight up the Aberqwesyn road and New Row. Number five was in a row of cottages on the left. I knocked on the door and went in calling out as I did so.

'Hello, is it the doctor? Please come in, Jennie is lying on the sofa in here' she led the way into the parlour. 'She's got chicken pox I think.'

'Hello Jennie, are your spots very itchy, how old are you?'

'She's ten,' said her mother, 'and I didn't know for certain what it was that was causing the spots. She's been staying with her cousin in Aberystwyth last week end and I think she picked it up there. 'How can you tell that it isn't smallpox?'

'There's no smallpox in this country just now' I said. 'But in any case she's been vaccinated hasn't she.'

'Thanks to a certain Dr Jenner who was a doctor in Gloucestershire at the beginning of the 1800s . He noticed that dairymaids who had suffered from a harmless complaint called vaccinia picked up from cows, were immune to smallpox. He found that he could give a person the cow pox by taking some of the liquid from the blister on a cow which had the disease and scratching it on to the skin of the person to be vaccinated. He then found that the vaccinated person was immune to smallpox.'

'So you've got chicken pox Jennie, and how are you feeling?'

'Oh I'm itching all over from these spots, and I am afraid of what will happen if I scratch them. One of the boys in school was teasing me and he said that if I scratched the spots I'd end up all scars like an old witch!'

'Well Jennie, that's all rubbish, you'll end up a lovely girl! Try not to scratch them though; I'll tell your Mum how to stop the itching and they'll all be gone in a few days anyway.'

'Mrs Hopkins, if Jennie finds the 'itchiness' is bothering her at night, let her lie in a nice warm bath for a few minutes, then when she is out of the bath and dry, dab her all over where the spots are, with calamine lotion.'

'I'll give you a prescription and you can get it from the chemist. You might also give her one or two teaspoonfuls of the medicine I will prescribe.' I wrote out the prescription for mist aspirin pro inf, the children's aspirin mixture, and some calamine lotion.

Reyes syndrome had not been described in the 1950s. One must not give children under twelve years old aspirin especially when they are suffering from a virus illness. Liver or brain damage can result though admittedly it is rare. Paracetamol was not available in the 1950s but it is best to use that nowadays.

I said goodbye and drove on, on the Abergwesyn road, looking for Penderlwn Goch, home of Jacob Owen. I found it without any difficulty; the name was on the gate. And it was set in the beautiful mountain countryside amongst the Welsh reservoirs: the small Llyn Berwyn and the large Llyn Brianne on the road to Llanwrtyd Wells.

I drove into the farmyard, the door of the house was open and I could see through into the kitchen where a woman was turning the handle of a churn.

'Hello,' I called, 'I've come to see Mr Owen. I'm told he's had an accident and hurt his back.'

'Oh good afternoon, is it the doctor? I was expecting to see Dr Alun. Is he away?'

'Yes, I'm Dr Frost-Smith. I'm acting while Dr Alun is away in London.'

'My husband is upstairs in bed. He has hurt his back. He slipped and fell backwards off a ladder. Mind you he was only standing on the first rung, so he didn't fall very far. Could you have a look at him please?'

'Olwen, Olwen! can you come down here please, dwi yn y Llaethdy (I am in the dairy).'

'Right Mam, rwy'n dod (I'm coming).'

'Olwen, when you feel the butter coming, call me, OK?'

'I make my own butter from the cream we get from our cows. You have to separate the milk with the separator, but the children help by turning the handle. They probably don't complain because they love the butter. Tea, bread and butter is our basic meal always.'

Mr Owen was lying in bed reading *The Western Mail*.

'Hello' I said. 'I've come to see you because I understand you've hurt your back. What happened?'

'Oh hello doctor. I understand that Dr Alun is away. Miss Davies said that I would be getting a young locum doctor. I'm Jacob Owen.'

Mrs Owen intervened. 'Come on boy, he knows that, tell him what happened to you. 'Long winded he is, you can never get him to the point!'

'Give him time now,' said I. 'So what happened Jacob?'

'Well, we keep hens you know, as well as everything else. I built the hen house myself. It was a hell of a job because I couldn't get the timber I needed. It's all on licence now. You'd never guess the war is over! You've got to get a permit or a licence for every bloody thing.'

I laughed. 'Well to be fair, the government is having to build all these houses to accommodate the men and women coming back from the war. I suppose they need all the building materials for that.'

'Don't tell me; this bloody Labour Government, too many regulations for my liking, and remember, it was the farmers that kept us afloat during the war. The bloody German U-boats were sinking all our ships carrying food.'

'Now then Jacob, the doctor hasn't got time to listen to your ravings! He never stops you know doctor, and every other word is bloody this and bloody that!'

'OK' I said, 'tell me then, so I understand you were repairing the chicken house.'

'Yes, that's right doctor. I'd only put one foot on the bloody ladder and the bottom rung broke. And I fell backwards on my arse. It wasn't a soft landing either. They were all laughing, Mam and the kids. It bloody well hurt! It wasn't funny!'

'No, It wasn't at all funny, but the language: well! and the kids had to hear it.'

'That's nothing Martha! You should hear the kids down at the Teifi Arms. Blinding and effing. I can tell you I'm a model of propriety compared to them.'

'Well then, you fell on your backside, did you?'

Yes and that was bad enough, but I heard somethin' crack and I was afraid I'd broken something.'

'Let's see: can you sit up please?'

'Yes indeed, I can do that.'

I looked at his back. There was the beginning of a big bruise starting over his sacrum and down to his anal region.

'Can you get out of bed for me?'

He slowly put his feet on the floor. I thumped his back fairly gently all the way down a few times, from his chest or upper lumbar area to the sacrum. At that point he grunted: 'It hurts there.'

'Stand up as straight as you can. Right: Now bend over slowly.' He found it painful at the base of his spine when he bent right over. I tried straight leg raising with him lying on his back and there was no evidence of sciatic nerve damage.

When I pressed over the very base of his spine, he groaned.

'I think you've cracked your coccyx'

'My what!'

'The remaining bones at the end of your spine. Your residual tail! It has very little function, and you won't need any treatment. It should settle down in a few days. Call me at the week end if it isn't a bit better.'

'I'm going to give you a prescription for some liniment and some tablets for the pain.' I wrote a prescription for Lin. Meth. Sal. (liniment of methyl salicylate). This would act as a counter irritant and block some of the pain. Also, some APC tablets, (aspirin phenacetin and caffeine).

'You can take two tablets if your pain is bad. Other wise just take one tablet three or four times a day. You can ask Martha to rub the liniment into your back.'

That was the last of my calls to see patients on Thursday. I drove back to the Talbot Hotel and found Marjorie in the sitting room reading a book on infant care.

'Now I don't think you really need to bother with that' I said. 'After the marvellous lectures and ward rounds with Pop Watkins.'

Professor Watkins was professor of paediatrics at Cardiff, and I'm sure we all benefited from his friendly and down to earth teaching on ward rounds and in outpatients.

'Yes, but this is a book about infant care, the advantages of breast feeding and regulation of diet. It's not about treatment of children's diseases.'

'OK, you're right of course. But I'm hungry, and I've just been seeing a patient on the Abergwesyn Road. It's a beautiful valley and the green hilly pastures are full of sheep with this year's lambs.'

'Well now, isn't that funny: It is just what you're going to have for dinner tonight. Welsh lamb and mint sauce!'

'You know, the tastiest and sweetest lamb is supposed to be from Herdwick sheep in Cumbria,' said I.

'It's probably true but I believe Welsh lamb comes close because of our wet climate and lush green grass on which the sheep feed.'

'Well let's go in to the dining room and eat!'

Friday morning. It's going to be quite busy. First I must call in at Rhydronnen and see whoever is there. Then I must go and see David Jones of Rose Cottage. When you get a bad pain in your chest, it rings alarm bells and you wonder what is happening to you.

Then Hannah Watkins. I hope that she is better having taken the sulpha pyridine. But I must be on time to meet Jim Williams at Llangwyryfon. I just wonder who thought up the great idea of free home consultations with consultant specialists. If the NHS develops as I think it will, I can see a few items and services that are available now being withdrawn.

When I got to Rhydronnen there were actually two patients waiting to see me and buying their groceries while they waited. Oh Lord I hope I'm not going to be kept long, I said to myself.

'Would you come in please' I said to the first. She came into the parlour and sat down. 'Hello, what can I do for you.'

'I was just buying a few things in the shop, but I really wanted to see the doctor. Is he away, are you standing in for him?'

'Yes, that's right. I'm afraid Dr Alun is away at present; but can I help you? I'm Dr Frost-Smith.'

'I don't know if you can. I think I've got a bad heart; I get this thumping in my chest. It frightens me.'

'I see. What is you name?'

'Gwyneth Robson.'

'Do you live in Tregaron?'

'No, I live in Bont (Pontrhydfendigaid), do you know it? I live at number four The Cottages. Just by Dickie Rees's shop.'

'Well you know, I have to come to Bont this evening. Would you like me to call in to see you. You can tell me about your problem and I'll examine your heart and give you a check up, then.'

'Oh thank you so much doctor. I have been so worried. I'll expect to see you later, about seven o'clock, is that right?'

'Yes, I'll be along later.'

The next patient to come in was a rather elderly man, looking worried.

'Hello. What can I do for you?'

'I've got a very itchy rash on my back and it's driving me mad, I can't get at it. Will you take a look at it please?'

'Could you take your shirt off, What is your name?' He pulled his shirt up.

'Dewi Williams. Look, I don't need to take it off; bloody hell it's cold in here. Wow! Look, it's just there!' He pointed with the back of his hand to an area on his back.

'Is it shingles I've got? My brother had the shingles a few years ago. Oh Mawredd! (glory be), he had a terrible time with it. It went up into his head and to his eye. It was so painful and he lost the sight of that eye you know. Could this be shingles that I've got; will it spread all over me? My missis saw it last night and she said: "Dewi, That rash looks nasty to me you go straight away to the doctor tomorrow morning. Where did you catch it?"

'I didn't catch it, it just came. "Well" she said "you go tomorrow first thing. It looks bad to me. Siwr y fod (Sure to be) that it's shingles." So here I am, bullied by my dear wife. I've got to do as I'm told you know!'

'Let me look at it,' said I. It was angry looking. 'Have you been scratching it?'

'Now, how could I scratch it, I can't get at it, I wish I could. The bloody thing is driving me mad especially at night.'

'Well something is scratching it,' said I. 'You've got a scratch rash, and that gets worse the more you scratch it!'

'Oh well I have been using a stone that's sticking out by the back door. It's just at the right height, and I'm like a cow scratching on a gate post!'

'This started because your skin is dry, very dry, it's just an age related condition. It's not infected and it's definitely not shingles. Now you mustn't scratch or rub it. I'll give you a prescription for some lotion to ease the situation. You can apply it as often as you like, probably two or three times a day. Get your wife to do it and let me know if it isn't better in a week.'

I prescribed some lotion – lotio calamine oleosa. It should help to soothe. There were no cortisone creams at that time. That was the last of my morning surgery patients. I must go and see Dafydd Jones at Rose Cottage now.

'Good Morning David. How do you feel today?' He was sitting up in bed and looking more relaxed. Little Enid is fussing around the bed.

'Mam, Mam,' she squeaked. 'Come upstairs, the doctor's here.' She ran to the door and shouts in a loud squeaky voice. 'Mam, can you hear me?'

'All right Cariad, I'm coming. These two kids will be the death of me, they're calling for something all the time.'

'Good morning doctor. I'm pleased to tell you that Dai has had a very good night. He's had some porridge this morning for his breakfast, and the only noises I've heard from this room this morning have been coming out of the mouth of this little one.' She gives Enid a little hug. 'All right Lodes fach, (Little Lady) you run downstairs now and make sure the potatoes are not boiling over' Enid runs off. 'She's dancing around her father all the time, can't leave him alone, and he just laps it up!'

'Now,' I said, 'lie down flat David and let me see your stomach.' I checked and all was OK. No rigidity, no tenderness. 'You're looking better' I said.

'Right, there's no need to stay in bed but I don't think you should go back to work yet. What is your work?'

'I am working in the quarry at Ystrad Meurig. I have to drive there every morning at seven o'clock. But we take it in turns, the three of us as to whose car we go in.'

'I'll give you an NHS certificate for a week, and then you come back to see me or Dr Alun, if he's back. Who owns the quarry?'

'Oh It's the council now, and they may want a private certificate if I'm off more than three days.'

'OK if they do need it, I'll give you one.'

'Oh thank you doctor.'

'Would you like a cup of tea before you go,' asked Martha.

'No thank you very much I must get along. I've still got a lot to do this morning, and there's the surgery in Bont this evening at seven o' clock. Cheerio to you both, a Pob Hwyl (and Good Luck).'

Now I must go to Llanddewi to see Hannah. I wonder how she is getting on; Blodwen let me in.

'I think you'll be pleased with her progress,' said she. 'Come upstairs, she's in bed. And what a fuss she's making. "Bring me this and bring me that." Now she wants a newspaper to see, she says, how the Labour Government is dealing with the new health service. We don't have a paper shop here. If we want anything like that we have to go into the town to Hughes The News he doesn't deliver out here.'

'Look,' I said I've got a *Western Mail* in the car. I bought it this morning and I've seen all I want to of it. Hannah can have it with pleasure.'

'Oh Da iawn (very good) and thanks. Now come up and see the patient.'

Hannah is looking much better and her chest sounds are approaching normal. Her temperature has come down to normal.

'Now then Hannah I'm pleased to see that you are better. I want you to continue with the M and B tablets for three days more, and I would like you to rest as much as possible.'

'When should I get up. I'm sick of lyin' here, and my sister is bossing me all the time.'

'Oh just stay here in bed today and get up tomorrow afternoon to a warm room. How's that?'

'Now I must hurry away, I'm sorry but I've got to be at Llangwyryfon by eleven thirty. Good bye to you both. I will call and see Hannah in a few days.'

I called in at the Talbot Hotel on the way and spoke to one of the staff. 'I'm having to go down to Langwyryfon now and I can't be back here before half past one or even two o'clock. I don't want to upset your schedule for the day, I'm afraid I can't help myself.'

'Oh don't you worry doctor. We'll give you your lunch when you get back. And shall I tell Mrs Frost-Smith; she'll probably want to wait and have her lunch with you.'

'Yes please and thanks so much. I must say, the service we are getting at the Talbot Hotel is outstanding.'

I found my way to Llangwyryfon Post Office, without losing my way. Megan was behind the counter and introduced herself.

'I've got Myfanwy here, she's in bed and waiting for you. I'm afraid she's in a bit of a state. She's worried I suppose. She knows very well that you wouldn't be bringing a specialist all the way out here from Aberystwyth if you didn't suspect that there is something serious going on.'

'I don't really know what to think. We'll have to wait to see what Mr Williams says when he has examined her. But I must warn you, that you won't get a firm answer today, but we'll set the wheels in motion for her to have a thorough check.'

There was the noise of a car door shutting and Mr Williams entered the shop.

'Hello, I assume you are Brian Frost-Smith.'

'Hello, yes and Brian will do thank you, and this is Mrs Megan Gael the patient's sister who is kindly letting us use her house.'

'Hello Mrs Gael. How do you find your sister?'

'Well, I don't see her all that much, but when we have met, and just recently, she has seemed 'washed out'; not a bit like her normal self. Possibly you are aware that she runs her smallholding almost single handed. It's not that she doesn't get help from the family. They are all hard workers. But she's obviously not quite herself.'

'Well that's very helpful and gives us an idea of what's going on,' said Mr Williams. 'Where is she now?'

'Come with me doctors, she's upstairs. I'll wait downstairs, if you want anything just shout.'

Mr Williams took a detailed history from Myfanwy, all the details of her life including her past illnesses, family history and all about her work and childbearing. He sat on the bed while doing this in a relaxed way that put Myfanwy at her ease and you could see the tension draining from her face.

His manner with the patient reminded me of the stories that went around medical students about taking a history from a patient. There have always been great charismatic teachers and their sayings, but so far as medical teaching is concerned I often think of two that have always seemed to me to be important when talking to and examining patients.

Professor, later, Lord Cohen who taught medical students that I knew in Liverpool, used, apparently to say repeatedly: 'Listen, listen, listen, the patient will tell you what is the matter with him.'

This may sound obvious, but on the many occasions on which I have been present during a domiciliary consultation, I have always been impressed by how the diagnosis emerges during the taking of the history. A diagnosis that has puzzled me even after careful examination of a patient has many times been clarified by this careful questioning. The consultant brought in to see the patient at home, and who is prepared to sit down and listen carefully and at length to the patient's story, without interrupting, often reveals the answer to the problem.

Times have changed however especially as far as hospital consultations are concerned. There are now so many radiological, biochemical and bacteriological tests that can be done, before the patient ever sees the consultant, and the diagnosis may be made clear before any sort of history is taken.

Jim Williams took great care in his gentle and sympathetic examination of Myfanwy, which related mainly to her symptoms and the early finding of a slightly enlarged uterus.

When he had finished, he said, 'Now Myfanwy, I am going to wash my hands and have a talk with Dr Frost-Smith. We'll come back then and discuss with you what we think is best for you.'

'Please, don't leave me in suspense. I've been so worried not knowing what is happening to me' Myfanwy said. 'Tell me the worst.'

' We'll come and discuss it with you in a moment,' said I.

'Now,' Jim said to me when we were out of earshot in the bathroom. 'I'm sure you know what I am going to say. As you rightly pointed out, a woman of this age with an enlarged uterus and irregular bleeding, cannot be ignored. The possibility of cancer of the uterus is a distinct possibility. As you know we cannot exclude it or confirm it without doing a D and C.' (dilatation and curettage: a diagnostic test in which a biopsy of the lining of the womb can be tested for abnormalities).

'I will take her in on Monday and do the D and C on Tuesday. I think in any case she should have a hysterectomy. Even if there is no malignancy. She is well past child bearing and the operation will give her a new lease of life. Would you like me to tell her that?'

'Thank you, I am happy with that,' said I.

We re-entered the bedroom to find Megan Gael, the patient's sister, sitting on the bed.

'Now Myfanwy you need to have some tests done so that we know exactly what is going on and so that we can treat you. I would like you to come into hospital on Monday. We'll get the tests done on Tuesday but I would recommend, whatever the results of the test that we remove your uterus. It is a straight forward operation and there should be no after effects.'

Myfanwy held her hands to her head and groaned: 'Oh Iesu Mawr (Great Jesus), you think it's cancer don't you! I don't see how I can come into hospital, Who is going to look after the farm and feed my family? I might as well die here and now.'

'Now hush, Myfanwy,' said Megan. 'We'll look after everything for you. You know that my husband, Dick is retired and he doesn't know what to do with himself. He spends too much time reading *The Racing News*. He will be pleased to come and feed the animals and look after everything for you at home. I'll come and give Alun his tea and Gwilym will be home at five o'clock every day and will take over so Dick can come home here.'

'I'll never get over this, I know I won't,' sighed Myfanwy.

'Look Cariad: don't you remember Mair y Capel (Mary of the Chapel). She had that operation last year, she's older than you and look at her now, she even goes to dances an' all! I will take you to Aberystwyth Hospital on Monday morning and see you settled.'

'Oh dyna fe (that's it) I'll have to do as I'm told. But thank you doctors and I am so sorry to have made such a fuss. I have complete confidence in you Dr, oh no it's Mr Williams isn't it? And I thank you too Dr Frost-Smith for everything.'

So we left Langwyryfon and I said goodbye to Jim Williams. He was a very pleasant man, I should think in his mid-40s. He has promised to let me know, probably on Tuesday, what he finds on examination of Myfanwy under anaesthetic. When a patient is under a short term anaesthetic, but deep enough to give complete relaxation, more can be ascertained and with less distress to the patient. At the same time a biopsy can be taken and the tissue obtained sent to the pathology laboratory. So there's nothing more that I can do until he phones me.

When I get to Tregaron, there will be just time to have a cup of tea before

I have to go to Bont to see what is waiting for me there. But my first call must be to Gwyneth Robson. That's not going to be easy if she has a fixation that she has a bad heart.

So I called in at the Talbot Hotel to see if there were any messages for me.

'Yes doctor,' said the man in the office. 'Miss Davies called and she said that Rev. Trimble had telephoned and asked if you would call at the Vicarage in Bont. He had said that his wife is not well and he thinks she may need some treatment. He also apologised for asking you to call; his wife is in bed and unable to come to the surgery.'

The Vicarage in Bont is on the right as you enter the village, so I'll call there first and I'd better be on my way now so that I have enough time. It's a straight run to Bont, about eight miles. I pulled in outside the Vicarage and rang the bell. After a moment the vicar came and opened the door. He was looking worried.

'Good evening doctor, thank you for coming so promptly. I think that Anne has had a sort of stroke. She can't speak properly, her words are slurred and the left side of her face is drooping. She's also dribbling saliva on that side and she cannot seem to control it.'

'I am sorry to hear that,' said I, 'is she upstairs in bed.'

He nodded, 'come this way please, up the stairs, It's the front room. You go first, would you like me to come too?'

'No' I said, 'you just come up to show me the way to her room.' I had never been inside the Bont Vicarage before, so I followed him and entered Mrs Trimble's bed room.

She was lying in bed and looking very sorry for herself. As the vicar had said the left side of her face was drooping with saliva running down her cheek.

'Oh doctor, I'm so glad you've come. I don't know what is happening to me.' This she said with slurred speech and in a sad way, almost a moan.

'Now Mrs Trimble, I'm sorry you are not well.'

'Oh, it's more than just not well,' said she. 'I can't speak properly and I'm sure I must be having a stroke. I've always feared this moment.'

'When did this start?' I asked.

'I am not sure, you see I've been worrying because my mother died of a stroke. She was only 58 when she had it, and she was an invalid for three years after that. My father had to look after her. Fortunately he was retired and was able to help her, but he died soon after she did. I'm sure the stress of looking after her played a part in his death.'

'What did your father die of?' I asked.

'He had cancer of the bowel.'

Taking a family history is very important. It does help to understand the patient and her proclivities. On the other hand one must not put too much weight on it.

'Mrs Trimble, How old are you?'

'I'm 51.'

'Have you had any serious illnesses, I really mean other than the children's ailments and colds and coughs?'

'No, I haven't had anything that you would call serious. Of course I've had two children, but that was straight forward enough, two boys, they're now in their twenties.'

'So when did this attack start?'

'Oh, you know how it is, just another day, I went down to Dick Rees to buy some groceries, and as soon as I entered the shop, someone said: "What's the matter with you face, Mrs Trimble, it's all twisted. What have you been doing? Here look in this mirror" I had a shock I can tell you. I felt all queer as if I was going to faint. Immediately my mind flashed back to my mama. She looked exactly the same when she had her stroke.

'"Now then: sit yourself down" said Dick Rees. Just then Alan White came into the shop; he's a church warden you know, so I know him well. "Come on Anne, what's the matter" said he, "you look as if you've seen a ghost." I think I've had a stroke, I must try and get home.

'"My car is just outside, come on I'll take you; is John at home in the vicarage?" I left him there, he's writing his sermon for next Sunday.

'So that's what happened to me. What do you think doctor?'

'Now, just lie down flat and look up at the ceiling.'

There was a slight droop to her left eyelid but her pupils were equal and reacting normally. I tested her arms and legs for power and movement and all were equal and normal, as was her grip in both hands. I used my car key to stroke the sole of her foot – the Babinski reflex –

down went her toes: normal!

The Babinski reflex was first described by a French neurologist, Joseph Babinski in 1896. If the big toe goes upwards when the sole of the foot is stroked firmly, the sign is positive. It indicates that there is upper motor neurone damage; that is a fault somewhere between the brain and the spinal cord, such as a stroke would produce. A stroke can be very severe, caused by the bursting, of an artery often the middle meningeal artery in the brain, producing an often massive paralysis of one side of the body and sometimes aphasia or inability to speak clearly, it can be less severe caused by a clot of blood or a thrombosis just causing a weakness on one side, or it can be quite mild and just caused by the spasm of a blood vessel.

Anne Trimble's condition didn't fit any of these. The only sign was a weakness of one side of her mouth and a drooping left eyelid.

'I think, Mrs Trimble, that you have not had a stroke.'

'Oh thank God, are you sure, why do you think that?'

'Well, you have no weakness in any of your limbs and there are, no signs suggesting a stroke.'

'Well, for goodness sake, what have I got then? Am I going to be like this for the rest of my life?'

'No, I am as certain as I can be that you will be back to normal in a few weeks. You have, what is called Bell's palsy.'

Bell's palsy was first described by Charles Bell, an Edinburgh anatomist in the early nineteenth century. It is a condition caused by inflammation of the facial nerve that supplies the muscles of the face. This nerve, the seventh cranial nerve travels through a small bony canal just under the ear. In Bell's palsy the nerve becomes swollen, possibly due to an infection causing paralysis of the muscles on that side of the face.

'What is the treatment doctor: will I have to give up smoking?'

'There is no treatment for this condition, it just gets better by itself. You must keep your eye from getting dry because you can't close that eye properly. I'll give you a prescription for some eye drops. Get your husband to put a drop or two in the eye two or three times a day to keep it moist. You could wear a patch or pad over that eye to protect it when you go outside.'

'Thank you doctor, you've done a good day's work; saved me from a life of hell, that's what. Where d'you come from? Oh don't tell me, I know, you are Mrs Frost-Smith's son from Hafod House, aren't you? My goodness I should have known. Just like your mother you are. Please give your mother my kind regards when you see her next.'

'I will do that, thank you and good bye. Let me know if you have any problems with it.'

Now for Gwyneth Robson. Her house is in a terrace just near Dickie Rees's shop.

'Hello,' I called as I entered by the front door which was open. A man appeared suddenly from the front room.

'Hello doctor please come in. I'm Wynne's husband, I'm Harry, and I've kept Wynne in bed 'cos I thought it would be easier for you to examine her. Could I just have a word before you see her? Come in this room here. That's right, please sit down for a moment. I just want to say, about Wynne. You know she's 48 and as far as I am aware she's quite well. She works hard looking after my daughter Ivy and me and she even does a few hours at the Red Lion for Mrs Foster and Edwin. But she honestly worries like hell. She is convinced she has a bad heart. She's never been ill and she doesn't behave like an invalid; she's full of energy. So I would be glad if you could examine her and talk to her. If there is anything wrong with her heart, I'll do my best to help.'

'What is your work, Harry?'

'I work at Pant y Fedwyn, you know, the community centre in Bont. I'm the manager. Shall I take you upstairs now, would you like me to stay while you examine her?'

'Yes please.'

'Hello again Mrs Robson. Now just tell me what it is that's worrying you.'

'Well I'm scared stiff that I've got a bad heart and every step I take I feel is going to be my last. My mother had a very bad heart, for as long as I can remember she was terribly short of breath and when she was only 45 she could hardly climb the stairs. She was only 49 when she died. Her heart failed and they said it was mitral stenosis caused by her having had rheumatic fever when she was twelve years old. I must admit I'm not ill like she was, but I have this terrible thumping in my chest: palpitation. It feels as if my heart is going to stop, it really does!

'My face flushes up as if I'm going to burst and then I fall into a fit of weeping until I feel I'm going mad. It's not fair on Harry and Ivy, our daughter. They are very kind and sympathetic and do their best for me.'

'Have you ever had rheumatic fever?' I asked.

'No, certainly not, I've never had any serious illness, not like my sister Jessie, she's always complaining of something.'

I noticed Harry's face, he raised his eyes upwards in a gesture of frustration.

'Well, I'd better have a look at you. You'll need to take your top off so I can see your chest properly. That's right, now lie down flat.'

I examined her chest front and back and her heart. There was an occasional extra beat, called an extra systole. I listened carefully particularly half way up the right side of the sternum (breast bone) to see if I could hear a murmur coming from the mitral valve. That is the valve on

This is Dickie Rees's shop. It was the only grocer shop in the village of Bont (Pontrhydfendigaid). During the war, one could not buy rationed food from just any grocer or butcher's shop. You had to buy from the shop with whom you were registered. Most villagers were registered with Dickie Rees, so he had captive customers. This is where the Branch Surgery was held twice a week.

the left side of the heart between the upper and lower chambers. This is a particularly difficult murmur to hear but once you've heard its soft rumble it's not forgotten. This sound indicates a partial blockage between the upper left part of the heart, the atrium and the lower chamber, the left ventricle.

This is mitral stenosis that Gwyneth's mother suffered from. It is commonly caused by rheumatic fever. It causes congestive heart failure, a very disabling complaint in which the patient's lips and fingers are blue due to the poor state of the blood and the congestion. Rheumatic fever is caused by a streptococcal infection of the throat. The limb joints are swollen and painful but the most serious effect is on the heart. 'It licks the joints and bites the heart,' is what they used to say. It is much less common today because a 'strep' throat, would be treated with penicillin and cured.

I examined Mrs Robson carefully including taking her blood pressure which was normal and making sure that there were no abnormal signs in heart or chest. She reported palpitations, and the extra systoles or a run of them would account for that.

'Now then Mrs Robson, Gwyneth; I have carefully examined you and I have to tell you that as far as I can tell your heart and chest are perfectly normal.'

'That's all very well doctor. If that is so, why am I getting these horrible thumps, like my heart is going to stop. There must be something wrong, surely.'

'Well, how old are you?'

'Well, I'm 48 next birthday, in December.'

'Are you still having regular periods?'

'Oh no, they went a bit irregular and now they've stopped. Before you say any more, I know I'm in the 'change'. I expected that. I'm a bit irritable sometimes, and I have the hot flushes.'

'Well I must say,' said I, 'as far as I can tell, there is nothing wrong with your heart and lungs. There are three factors I can think of, that may be responsible for the palpitations, but first I must explain the normal regular heart beat.

'The heart beat starts from a small area at the upper end of the heart that sends out a regular 'bleep'. It is an electrical impulse and it spreads down the heart making it contract. Several things may upset the regularity of this bleep. The point is, that after every beat there is a period when the heart is relaxed and resting. If for some reason there is an extra beat then there is an extra long period of delay. This is frightening to the patient. It feels for a moment as if the heart has stopped. Some of the possible causes are, changes due to the menopause, too much strong coffee and too much smoking.'

'Well' said Gwyneth, 'that may be it then: I'm in the 'change', I love strong coffee when I can get it and yes, I have to confess I am smoking much more.'

'So it is possible you can improve the situation by cutting down the cigarettes and the coffee. This may not stop the palpitations completely but there could be an improvement. But the main thing is: You haven't got a bad heart. If you still feel upset and anxious in three months I think you should go back to Dr Alun and see what he says. I am pretty sure that what I have suggested is right.'

There were, as I said, no real symptoms of heart disease nor were there any signs that I could detect. I must admit, that today there are a whole host of investigations that would be appropriate if the patient remained worried: ECG (electrocardiogram), cardiac enzymes, echo cardiogram and others which require specialist intervention. In my time as a GP I found it well nigh impossible to convince some patients that their heart was normal. The training we had, particularly from Dr Byron Evans was first class and down to earth; but that was, in my case 67 years ago! All GPs try to keep up to date by informative meetings and reading, but technical advances, these days, come so rapidly that it can be difficult to keep in touch with what is available.

The evening surgery in Bont was held in the sitting room of Dickie Rees's house, next door to the shop. I entered through the shop where there were a few customers waiting to be served. The shop stayed open until quite late, especially during the war years. A very large number of families were registered here and often there were queues of customers waiting outside the shop. I think it was because Dick Rees was able to supply a very good variety of groceries. Rationing was still in force at the time of which I am writing.

I pushed gently past the folk waiting in the shop. Someone opened a door into the house and led me to the sitting room where I was to see patients. The first was a tall late middle aged lady who didn't look happy.

'Good evening' said I. 'What can I do for you?'

'Where's the doctor, I came here to see Dr Alun, I'm not at all well. Are you a doctor? Well, I have come all the way from Pengarreg on the bus to see him and he's not here.'

'I'm sorry' said I, 'I'm afraid Dr Alun is away in London. Can I help you at all?'

'Oh I don't know, he told me to come back here today, and here I am; all that way I've come and he's not here! Are you a doctor, you look too young. I don't know if you can do anything for me.' My age again I thought – will I ever grow up? The lady spoke with a marked German or Polish accent.

'I'm Dr Frost-Smith, what is your name please?'

'I'm Mrs Pachini, and I'm having terrible pain in both my knees. I can hardly walk; something will have to be done. My husband is complaining. He can't speak much English and I have to do everything. Oh God I wish I had never come to this country!'

'Mrs Pachini, could you lie down on this couch please. Let me see your knees. Oh dear they are both swollen with fluid in the joint. Could you take your stockings off so I can see your knees properly'

'It's very cold in here haven't you got any heat on?'

'It won't take long if you could just let me see your knees.'

Both knees were swollen with fluid and when I bent them they creaked, and she was obviously in pain.

'You have arthritis in both your knees Mrs Pachini. There is no cure, but I will prescribe some tablets for you, I will give you cream to rub into your knees and I will give you a prescription for some crêpe bandages.'

I wrote a prescription for some rheumasan cream, some codeine tablets and some three inch crêpe bandages.

'Can you bind up your knees with the bandages if I prescribe them for you?'

'I think I can manage that' said she, 'but I don't suppose it'll help much.'

'I think you should rub the cream into the knees and bind them firmly, and you can take one of the tablets three times a day, no more than that please!' She walked out without a word!

There was only one more patient. He came in with his mother.

'Doctor please will you look at Gareth's leg, he's got somthin' growin' out of it. I'm afraid it might be a growth, cancer you know. These boys, they'll be the death of me!'

Gareth aged about twelve was looking sorry for himself.

'Leave it mam, it's OK.'

'Now you just show the doctor your leg Gareth.'

He pulled up the left leg of his trousers. On the inside of the tibial area was a small white object the size of a small pea.

'You don't know what that is?' I asked.

'No they both said in unison.'

'You don't live here, in the country then?'

'No, we're staying with friends here, we're from Birmingham.'

'Well, that explains why you are not familiar with this creature. It's a sheep tic.'

I picked out my forceps from my bag. 'Hold still.'

'Hey, what you gonna do!' cried Gareth.

I took hold of the tic as low down as I could and pulled it out. I had got it complete, legs and all.

'There you are,' I said, 'there's your growth!'

'What in heaven's name is that?' cried Mrs Owen.

'That is a common sheep tic. It's an arthropod, like a spider. It has four stages to its life cycle: it starts as an egg that hatches into a larva which attaches itself to a small animal in grass and heather. Then it develops into a nymph that clings to a sheep, and then this grows into an adult that climbs on to a human. It feeds on the blood of its host. The commonest complication for the human host is called Lyme disease, that humans can catch from the tic. It is caused by a bacteria.'

'Well thank you doctor,' said Mrs Owen, 'for that bit of information but more for getting rid of that horror.'

'Just bathe the sore spot with a little antiseptic and Gareth will be quite all right.'

'Now you just thank the doctor, Gareth, for getting rid of that tic.'

'Thanks doctor, very much, but ugh, it gives me the shivers!'

That was the end of that little adventure in the small village of Bont. It was nearly nine o'clock before I got back to The Talbot. They knew I would be late, Marjorie had waited for me and the hotel had laid on a lovely cold supper. By that time I was really hungry and tucked greedily.

We had a quiet night, there were no calls and we slept soundly, awoken by the noise in the market square at about seven thirty. Although it was Saturday morning I still had to go to Rhydronnen to see any patients that came to see a doctor. For the first few years that I was in practice, we and many other GPs had a morning and an evening surgery on Saturdays; we took it for granted. General practice was a seven day per week institution.

We went to see my parents on Saturday afternoon. I left their telephone number with the Talbot in case I was needed. We drove up the lane to Hafod, the fairly large house that father and mother had retired to. It was rented from Margery Lloyd, a distant relative. It had plenty of space and a big garden for my mother to grow her vegetables and fruit. It also had plenty of out buildings, the largest of which my father used as his workshop for the manufacture and set up of his beloved Electrano; and that, was doing very well indeed as a retirement job.

We all had tea and exchanged news. Mother had made some pikelets as she called the small pancakes hot with butter running through them. Yum! delicious. We got back to the Talbot Hotel in time to enjoy the cold supper that had been left for us.

I promised to call and see Tommy Evans at 4 Teifi Way on Sunday morning. To my surprise I found he was still in bed at ten o'clock.

'Oh doctor I'm afraid he's had a bad night again' said his mother. 'I don't understand it: he woke at about three this morning and was wheezing badly. I gave him a whole tablet, I know you said just half, but he was so bad, and I didn't want to send for you again. Anyway he improved quite quickly. I think those tablets are marvellous,' said she, 'but I thought he'd better have the morning in bed to get a little sleep after his restless night.'

'Let's have a look at him' said I.

'Tommy, the doctor's here,' called Mrs Evans. 'Come on upstairs, doctor, he's probably asleep.'

Tommy was asleep breathing quietly and regularly, but as soon as we went into the room he sat up in bed.

'I wasn't asleep Mam, I just had my eyes closed.'

'Hello Tommy,' said I 'How do you feel now?'

'Oh I'm OKthanks.'

'You had a bad night, I'm told. What were you doing last evening?' I asked.

'Nothing much really. I went for a walk down the Wenallt with Eirion.'

'Is that your girlfriend?' He blushed.

'Oh' said Mrs Evans, 'that's it. Now I understand what's happened. Eirion is a really nice girl, Tommy and she are in the same form at school. But she works on Saturdays at Wyn Griffiths Turkey Farm. I bet her coat is covered in bits of turkey feathers.'

'Oh golly, I thought she smelled funny,' said Tommy with a grin.

'If you were close enough to her to smell the turkeys. no wonder you breathed in some of the feathers,' said his mother.

'OK, next time we go for a walk I'll ask her to put a different coat on; yes Mam?

'You just watch yourself Thomas, you were quite ill, needlessly. You tell him doctor.'

'I think you are quite right and I am sure that Tommy understands now.'

'Goodbye Doctor and thank you said Tommy, 'I'll leave the feathers and keep the girl.'

All the pubs in Wales were closed on Sundays at this time. That was probably the influence of the Methodist Church in Wales but being a resident I was able to have a beer with my supper. In 1961 the Welsh counties were able to decide for themselves whether to open their pubs on Sundays. In some counties it was decided to remain dry, but in others, as in South Wales the Sunday closing rule was relaxed.

It wasn't just the pubs that were closed on Sundays in Cardiganshire.

Everything shut down except for the churches. Sometimes on a Sunday, during the war when father was at home he would want to send off some memos that he had put off writing until Sunday; a last minute job!

He would leave it until the last minute and by then the only outgoing post was from Aberystwyth. Of course I loved driving the car so I would volunteer to take his letters and it was a good excuse to drive. Driving cars during the war was only allowed for official business. The 'basic' petrol allowance ceased in the early 1940s. A small amount of petrol could be obtained only by using the official E coupons issued to people with an official job connected with the war effort. Father was supplied with these E coupons for his work as an HMI, but he certainly wouldn't dare use them for pleasure motoring. The jaunt to Aber' although just a fun drive for us would be regarded as official business. We would post the letters in the Post Office in Great Darkgate Street and then go for a spin along the Prom. I noticed that there were quite a few gift shops and sweet and tobacco shops open. There wouldn't be another car in sight unless it was a delivery van or Post Office van. We were never stopped, but if a policeman had seen three young lads driving along and obviously having a jolly time, he would probably have stopped us and asked for our credentials. We were free of guilt and did not worry.

On the next day, Monday I was going to follow up on three patients: the first was David Jones of Rose Cottage.

'Good morning' I called as I entered Rose Cottage. 'Where are you David?'

'I'm here in the parlour, come in doctor. I'm feeling much better, the pain has gone, but I've had a letter from the hospital: I'm to attend Medical Outpatients to see Dr Maurice Jones next week. We are all a bit worried about what he is going to say.'

'Dr Maurice is a physician who specialises in gastro-intestinal medicine. I can tell you for certain that he is going to try his best to help you without resorting to surgery. So don't worry.'

'Well that's good news, I'll call Meg.'

'Meg, Meg! Dere yma (please come here), dod i mewnn i'r parlwr (come to the parlour).'

'O Duw, beth s'yn bod yn awr? (O Lord what's the matter now?)'

'The doctor's here.'

'Oh, sorry, I thought something was wrong. Hello doctor, they've got me on pins here. Is everything all right?'

'Yes absolutely,' said I. 'I was just reassuring David that he is not going to be plunged into an operation without a great deal of thought by the specialists. Operation is a long way off and will most probably not be needed. I do feel that we need some expert guidance however on how to treat you in the best way.'

'Thank you doctor, I feel better for that.'

'Now you must keep in touch with Dr Alun; don't wait until you're in pain before you see him next.'

I won't hear anything from Jim Williams until Tuesday when he has promised to 'phone me at the Talbot Hotel around eight in the evening.

On Monday evening after we had had our dinner, a call came in for me. It came direct to me. Miss Davies at Dr Alun's house had told the caller where to find me. The waiter in the dining room called me to the telephone and I picked up the receiver.

'Hello, this is Dr Frost-Smith speaking, is it me you want?'

The caller sounded very Welsh and he started straight away speaking in Welsh, far too rapid and difficult for me to understand.

'Excuse me, my Welsh is not very good, could you repeat what you said in English?'

'Oh sorry I thought I was talking to Dr Alun. Is he away, are you the doctor?'

'Yes, I am Dr Frost-Smith, how can I help you?

'Oh dear I can see this is going to be difficult. I'm calling about my son, Alan. He has been ill all day; he's been vomiting and he has a pain in his stomach, a pretty bad pain, it seems. Can you come out to see him. I think it's quite urgent!'

'Yes of course I'll come straight away. Where do you live?'

'Do you know the road to Ponrhydfendigaid, the road to Bont you know. Well about four miles along, there is a turn right, It's the only turning right and it is just opposite the Abbey Farm.'

'Oh I know where Abbey Farm is'

'Well turn up that road, it's quite rough, so go carefully and about a mile along, there is a turning left. It has a 'No Through Road' sign but there is also a small sign with the name of our house from where I am 'phoning you now. The house is called Pen Bryn. You can drive the first half mile up the road. but then, you must walk, only a tractor can go the last hundred yards. Do you think you can manage?'

'Yes, will you please leave a light on in the house so that I can see where I'm supposed to be going.'

'We will keep a look out for you.'

Delivery men and other callers like doctors don't know they're born today with sat navs and mobile phones!

I set off at once and soon found the turning opposite Abbey Farm. That was where my troubles started! I drove about a mile up a very rough road, the brave little Ford Prefect behaving splendidly. I could see no left turn. It was a dark night and the headlights did not give a very clear view of the side of the road. A little further on I noticed a gap in the side of the road, it looked like a lane. This must be it, I thought. Before I had travelled twenty yards I could see I was in the wrong place. The road became little more than bridle way: no hope of going further.

Now I had another problem – the reversing lights were dim, and the rear window of the Prefect small, and by this time was clouded over; and I was in a hurry to see a sick patient. 'Oh my God! Help!' Is there a patron saint for doctors or must I make do with St Christopher. I prayed silently. There was obviously no help on this cold miserable dark night.

"You must learn to manage" said Florence Nightingale to her nurses in the Crimean War. All right! I got out and immediately stepped in a deep puddle. This poor little car is going to be in a mess by the time I've finished with this adventure. I examined the road behind me for possible obstacles and gently reversed the car back the way I had come. I was lucky, I hit the proper road without further trouble. I still had to find the little lane with the sign to Pen Bryn. I drove back carefully, and then I saw it; the sign facing this way so the lights of the car picked it out. I drove up gingerly. It was as the caller had said: the road stopped and there was a turning circle.

I walked the rest of the way up to the house, the lights were on and the door open. A woman appeared looking anxious. 'Have you had a bad time doctor, finding us?'

'Well, yes but I made it after a slight set back. Now, this is your son who is ill. How old is he and what is his name?'

'He is Alan Phillips and I am Mrs Phillips, his mother. He is eighteen and he works with his father in the Forestry. Come this way please.' Alan was lying on his left side in bed, curled up and looking pale.

'Now then Ally the doctor's come to see you.'

'Could you lie on your back please?' I said to him. 'Now where is the pain?'

He pointed to his navel, in the centre of his abdomen. 'It started here yesterday and I thought it was just colic. but then it got worse and seemed to move to down here,' he pointed to the Macburney area, (site of the appendix).

'Did you vomit?'

'Oh yes two or three times, I thought I had food poisoning but I didn't have any diarrhoea. In fact I haven't had a poo for two days.'

There was marked tenderness over the area where one would expect to find his appendix. There was also some rebound pain, a sharp jab of pain felt when you suddenly release the pressure of your hand from the abdominal wall, a sign of peritoneal irritation. Examination rectally revealed extreme tenderness high up the rectum. He had a fever of 100 degrees Fahrenheit (37.7 degrees Celsius).

'Well' said I, 'Alan has all the symptoms and signs of acute inflammation of his appendix. He will have to go into hospital and have his appendix out, immediately.'

'Can we not wait a day or so to see if it improves? This is so sudden; I must say we were not prepared for this. We thought he had food poisoning.'

'The danger of waiting is that this will certainly not go away and in fact it could get a lot more serious. His appendix is like a ripe boil about to burst. If that happened he would have acute peritonitis; a much more serious and dangerous condition.'

'Say no more' said his mother. 'Ally must go into hospital straight away. Will he have to go tonight?'

'Oh yes, I think there is do doubt about that. He will be seen at the hospital tonight and the surgeon will probably operate tonight or early tomorrow and remove the inflamed appendix. I will telephone from here if I may.'

'I'll take you to the 'phone, it's in the kitchen.'

I gave detailed directions to the ambulance, how to reach Pen Bryn, and the name and age of the patient.

'How far have we to carry the stretcher from the end of the road to the house,' asked the ambulance man.

'Oh about two hundred yards, will that be all right?'

'Bloody hell, isn't there a road to this farm?'

'Afraid not, I hope you will be able to cope.'

'Leave it to us, we've been in worse places. We'll be there in about two hours.'

Home at last to the Talbot and I sank into bed praying that there would be no more calls that night.

On Tuesday morning, I am on pins waiting to hear the report from Jim Williams about Myfanwy. I can't stop thinking about the hard life that these small hill farmers lead. Myfanwy was typical of many families who lead a simple life on small holdings. During my early teenage years, in Wales I knew of quite a number of families where this was their way of life. If Myfanwy became ill or disabled it would have a serious impact on their income and their stability as a family unit.

So every thing depends on what is happening in her uterus. If indeed she has uterine cancer it is possible that the growth will have spread into other tissues adjacent to her uterus. This is a particular worry because she and her sister had both said that she had been suffering like this for a long time, afraid to find out the truth of what was causing the trouble.

At Rhydronnen that morning there were just a few patients to see the doctor. Mrs Lewis a next door neighbour of the Hopkins' at New Row came in looking agitated.

'What's the trouble Mrs Lewis?' I asked.

'I've rushed here from home and left my little son yelling his head off. He says there are insects crawling all over him!'

'Is there anything on his skin'

'Oh yes, he's covered in spots and he's trying to scratch them. I've told him he mustn't touch them or he might get covered in scars, and now he's terrified.'

'How old is he?'

'He is five and a bit, it was his birthday last week and he had a party.

It was a couple of days after, that he was sick and he wouldn't eat. Can you come and see him doctor? I must rush back to make sure he's all right.'

'I will come immediately after the surgery is finished, in about twenty minutes. I think I know what is happening, so don't worry. Go on home now and I'll be along very soon.'

She left, and a middle aged man came in looking harassed.

'I'm sorry to take up your time doctor, but I'm at my wits end. We haven't met I know, but I am Gwilym Jenkins, Myfanwy's husband. My son, Alun and I went to see Myfanwy in Aber Hospital last evening, She was in Ceri ward. It was visiting time so the ward sister let us in to see her. I was really upset when we came to her bed; she looked so ill and drawn, I just wondered what is going to happen: is she going to get over this illness? I am asking your opinion because I need to make plans about the farm.'

'I cannot tell you very much at the moment; I know you understand that she is very ill and that this has been going on for some time. I am afraid that it will not be possible to answer your question until Mr Williams, the gynaecologist has completed the tests. We should have some idea of how she is going to be by tomorrow evening. Until then, I am afraid you must wait for that. I am sorry, I know how difficult it must be for you and your son.'

'Well I understand exactly what you are saying but I do want to explain why I have come to ask you.'

'I believe you are aware that Myfanwy runs our small holding on her own while I am at work for the council. I think you know that we are tenants of Harrison Estates. Well you may not know that Mr Harrison who is the owner of all the farms that are part of the estate, has died recently.'

'No, I am sorry I did not know that. How is this going to affect you both?'

'The estate is in the hands of trustees. There are huge death duties to pay to the government. In order to pay this large sum, I don't know how much it is, but I have been told that some farms and houses are to be sold. The agent for the trustees has written to me and asked if we would like to buy our little farm.'

'I think I understand what you are saying,' said I. 'If Myfanwy is going to be in poor health for a long time you would have to say no to the offer and, if the worst were to happen, you might have to give up the farm entirely.'

'I can't bear to think of it,' said he in a shaking voice. 'Myfanwy knows what is going on and she keeps on telling me to drop the whole thing, that she is afraid she's going to die. You know doctor, she has put her whole life into looking after our son Alun and that small farm. She has worked without help without   complaint ever since we took it on 25 years ago and I can't bear to think that this is going to be her reward.'

'Now Gwilym you mustn't give up hope yet. Just hold on until we get some news from Mr Williams.'

'We have been given an asking price by the agent' said he. 'In consideration of the fact that we are tenants. They have valued the smallholding complete at £1,400. I have worked out the details and with the money that my mother left me five years ago, and a loan from my brother who has a business in London, together with a small mortgage that I can get from the Farmer's Union, we could think about buying it.'

'Well,' I said 'please don't ask me about the advisability of going ahead with the purchase of the farm, your solicitor is the right person to advise on that. But I will do my best to guide you and inform you about the outlook for Myfanwy. Please do try to think positively.'

'I have consulted my solicitor, doctor, and his advice is that I must wait to see how Myfanwy is, and he thinks that if it should happen that all is well we should put in an offer of £1,200.'

'There it is then. We'll just have to wait until tomorrow and I will be in touch with you as soon as I have any news. Let us pray that there is no bad news.'

'Amen to that then,' said Gwilym, and he left.

During my time living in Wales I got a distinct impression that the ordinary Welsh men and women in ordinary jobs, in Cardiganshire spoke better English than their counterparts in England. There seemed to be a sort of poetry and precision in their utterances. Also a sort of musicality. Be that as it may. Actually, during my life as a GP I was frequently asked to advise on procedures that had little to do with medicine!

The next call was on Mrs Lewis and Dewi at 6 New Row. I could hear the crying and some screaming before I entered the house. Little Dewi was lying on the floor rolling around and yelling his head off.

'Now then Dewi sit up and say hullo to the doctor who has come to see you. He's going to make you better.' The crying   increased somewhat and he rolled onto his side away from me.

'Don't worry Mrs Lewis, I can see what it is. He's got chicken pox.'

'You will know of course that little Jenny next door has got chicken pox too. I am sure he has caught it from her at the party he had. Jenny was here you said.'

'I wasn't sure what Jenny was suffering from, but I do understand now; it's very infectious isn't it?'

'Yes, it is and there is no specific treatment, though I imagine in a good few years we will be immunising against most of these 'childhood' diseases. In the meantime, I will give you some medicine to ease the irritation and some lotion. I gave Mrs Lewis the advice about applying the lotion and directions for taking the mist aspirin pro inf.

In the afternoon I had to go to Llangwyryfon at the usual time, but in the morning I had not received any new calls. I called in at the Talbot Hotel thinking that it was a good time to have a cup of coffee with Marjorie. During the war years there was very little coffee around because it had to be imported and there were more important items to think about that had to be brought in by the gallant men of our Merchant Navy. We had Camp Coffee sometimes at home. It had a distinctive taste and contained chicory. I don't know what else it had in it. But tea was the main drink at that time and it became famous for its restorative powers at times of crisis: 'the Cup That Cheers, But Not Inebriates.'

I was just about to ask at the bar for some coffee for us both when one of the staff called out to me from the office: 'Doctor, there is an urgent call; Miss Davies has just 'phoned and asked you to go as soon as possible to Llangeitho. It's a patient called Mr Harry Bevan. The address is Oak Cottage, Sea Street, Llangeitho. The caller said it's urgent they think he's having a heart attack.'

I made sure that my bag was in the car and drove off without delay. It is only about four miles to Llangeitho and I was there in about fifteen minutes. Oak House is right in the centre of the large village and the name is clear on the front door. I knocked loudly and went in calling,

'Hello, it's the doctor.'

A woman came running to the door. 'Come upstairs doctor, he's in bed and he's in such pain, right in his chest. He has been having pains in his chest on and off for some time and Dr Alun said it was angina and he gave him some little tablets to put under his tongue when he got an attack. He has done that twice but it hasn't stopped the pain.'

'Here we are, in here.'

'Harry, here's the doctor come to see you, Doctor Frost-Smith is it? Miss Davies said that Dr Alun is away and that you would be coming. Harry is 68 and retired from the quarry.'

'Mrs Bevan, will you please boil the kettle with about half a pint of water and tell me when it is boiling. I might need to sterilise a syringe.' Mr Bevan was lying half upright on pillows, clutching his chest and groaning.

'Oh doctor, for God's sake can you help me; this bloody pain will finish me off if it can't be stopped. I know its my heart, Doctor Alun warned me this could happen.'

'Does the pain go down you arm' I asked.

'Oh hell yes, right down my left arm. I've had this sort of pain before. He said it is angina, from my heart. But it's never been as bad as this.'

I listened to his heart, but could not make out much. His Blood pressure was much lower than it should have been in a man of 68.

'I'm going to give you an injection. Can you pull your sleeve right up please.'

Mrs Bevan called from downstairs 'The kettle is boiling doctor.'

I put the syringe and a new needle in a basin and poured the boiling water over them. When they were cool, I prepared an ampoule of ten milligrams diamorphine hydrochloride with distilled water.

When I put a tight band around his upper arm a good vein appeared in his cubital fossa. That is the inside of the bent elbow. The needle went into the vein easily and I very slowly injected the whole of the contents of the syringe. I watched his face closely while the injection went in. It always filled me with wonder and pleasure to see the tension draining from his face, and almost a relaxed smile began to appear.

'Oh my God, that's wonderful. I could go to sleep easily now.'

'I am going to have to send you into hospital straight away, Harry. It is most important that you are under hospital care for the next week or so. I'll send for an ambulance to take you in.'

'Do you have a telephone Mrs Bevan?'

'It's by the front door downstairs.'

I phoned the ambulance station at Aberystwyth and was pleased and surprised when the operator said that he was in radio touch with the ambulance and that they were at Penuwch, just a couple of miles down the road from Llangeitho.

'They'll be with you in ten minutes, and doctor, please leave a letter with the clinical details and most importantly if you have given him any medication, please say what and when, you gave it.' I immediately telephoned the hospital and made sure that a bed was available. Then I wrote the required letter. I explained to Mrs Bevan what I had done and she, of course understood and was greatly relieved.

So that was the end of that drama. But I must explain that at that time there was no such thing as a defibrillator to restart a stopped heart. In the event of a cardiac arrest, cardiac massage was the only hopeful remedy available. Also, there were none of the most important helpful means of treating a blocked coronary artery like so called 'clot busting drugs' and the other anticoagulants, in life saving use today. In addition to that I don't think that it was possible in those days to pass a catheter into the arteries of the heart and put in place a stent to keep the blood flowing. Many, if not most patients suffering a not too severe coronary thrombosis, would be treated conservatively at home, especially in country areas.

I drove back to Tregaron, satisfied that Harry Bevan would be in good hands at Aberystwyrh Hospital. Today, we would say 'give up smoking' to anyone, and much more so to a patient who has heart or lung disease; but not at the time I am describing. The research linking tobacco smoking to cancer of the lung only commenced in 1950 and continued until 2001.

In 1948 we, as medical students were told that King George VI was suffering from Buerger's disease, a condition which affects the arteries and mainly the circulation in the lower limbs. He had an operation involving removal of special nerves intended to relieve the effects of the disease. It was only partly successful and the king was advised to give up smoking. He refused to do this and he died in 1952. It was well known that smoking caused this disease, but smoking was considered generally to be beneficial. Today, as we all know, the places where one may smoke is enforced rigidly by law, but if you had told someone in 1950 that this would happen it would have caused great amusement.

This was not uppermost in my mind as I drove back to have lunch. I was thinking mainly of what a catastrophe it would be for Gwilym and Myfanwy if she was found to be suffering from cancer of the womb. As we had lunch I unburdened some of my fears on to Marjorie.

'Well,' she said. 'This is only the beginning for you, this is what general practice is all about. You've only been here just over a week and already you've had to deal with some quite difficult problems.

'Not just medical problems but ones affecting the happiness and future of patients. The only work that I have done has been as a hospital doctor. I can understand that as a GP you are going to be much closer to the whole family than you would be working in other branches of medicine. You have to act, not only as a medical scientist but also as an adviser, comforter and friend. In doing this you must not try to take on the burdens and worries of the patients that you treat.' As usual this was good advice, as I was to find out later in my life.

Later on I went down to Llangwyryfon, but on the way I called in to ask Mrs Bevan if Harry's admission to the hospital had gone smoothly.

'Yes' she said. 'He was quite comfortable when I 'phoned, and the doctor was with him.'

'Give him my best wishes when you see him,' I said.

There was only one patient waiting at Tynarfon to see me. A repeat prescription for some cough medicine. I couldn't tell which of Dr Alun's favourites had been prescribed. But the patient said he had a dry cough that kept him awake at night, so I wrote a script for some 'Gee's Linctus' (linctus scillae opiate) and promised that it would be sent down on the bus that evening.

When I got back to Tegaron I made my way to see Hannah at Llanddewi to see how she was getting on with her M and B tablets. She should be a lot better by now.

The two ladies at Bryn yr Afon were sitting in the parlour. Blodwen was knitting and Hannah was reading Tuesday's *Western Mail*. They both looked up in surprise when I entered the room, tapping lightly on the door as I went in.

'Oh hello doctor, thank you for calling. How are you getting on; you're busy I expect.'

I smiled ruefully. 'Yes, I rather wish I had taken more trouble to learn to speak Welsh better. But I am managing very well really thank you and what about you Hannah, are you feeling better?'

'You needn't ask her' said Blodwen, 'I know she's better. She's arguing with me all the time, and she's hardly coughing at all. Like our mother, she is: talk, talk, talk; I can't get a word in edgewise.'

'It's all very well for you Blodwen,' said Hannah. 'But I'm worried about what this Labour Government is doing. This Aneurin Bevan: there's no doubt that he has brought in a wonderful Free Health Service. It had to come, but everything: glasses, false teeth, almost anything the doctor writes on that prescription pad of his, must be supplied free. Even specially made shoes. It won't last you know; I'm sure of it. Someone will have to pay for it, and I know who it will be, the tax payer. Blod and I have worked hard all our lives and saved carefully. But there's no point in saving when the government hands it out virtually, to anyone who asks.'

'Now ladies! I am glad to hear that you have improved Hannah. But I'm afraid I can't join in this political argument; I'm too busy. You look after yourself Hannah, and you too Blodwen. And just remember that if you need glasses or dentures you should be able to have them even if you can't afford to buy them yourself. No one in their senses would demand these thing if they didn't really need them.'

I went out quickly before Hannah had time to reply. By then it was nearly dinner time. I made my way to the hotel and met Marjorie in the sitting room.

'Have you finished knitting those Pilches yet?' I asked.

'No, I've given up. I can see knitting is not my strong point. Your mother said she would finish them for me, so I've been improving my mind reading *Wuthering Heights* again. And I went for twenty minutes walk.'

'Well I'm expecting this call from Mr Williams but he said about eight o'clock. So we might as well go in for our meal.' We were more than half way through the meal when the waiter approached the table.

'Doctor, can you come to the telephone please? It's a lady, she says her name is Margaret Roderick and she is Mr Williams' secretary.' I felt very nervous suddenly. I dropped my knife and fork and rose to my feet.

'Steady now Brian,' said Marjorie, 'you must be calm and collected. Go and speak to her and come back and tell me what she says.'

'Hello, Dr Frost-Smith speaking. Is Mr Williams wanting to speak to me?'

'Well no actually he is trying to contact Mr Gwilym Jenkins, Myfanwy Jenkins' husband.'

'What is the problem?' I asked.

'I have been getting no reply from his home 'phone number. I've tried several times and I also contacted Myfanwy's sister at Llangwyryfon Post Office. Mrs Gael says she has no idea where he could be. She said she was worried about him. She said she knows he is having a worrying time, but he has been depressed before when their son Alun was born.'

'Could you leave me Mr Williams' telephone number so that I can let him know what is happening?'

I decided to go down to see Megan at the Post Office to see if there was any news of Gwilym. I had nearly finished my dinner and I didn't bother with pudding or coffee. I explained the situation to Marjorie and set off.

'He was really depressed when Alun was born, Megan told me. At the time he thought he was going to lose both his wife and the baby. She did have quite a difficult time with the confinement, but he couldn't seem to come to terms with reality. For a couple of weeks while Myfanwy was in hospital we had to watch him carefully to make sure he didn't harm himself. Now Dick has gone down to the farm to try and find him. I've asked Dick to take him home when he finds him and to 'phone me here.'

The 'phone rang just as she was speaking.

'Hello Dick, have you found Gwilym?'

'He's here with me now. I found him down by the river. He was a bit dazed and kept saying that he couldn't go on if Myfanwy was not going to get better. I managed to bring him back to the house and I have made him a cup of tea. I have told him that Mr Williams wants to talk to him, but he just held his head in his hands and sobbed.

"'I know it's bad news," he said. "The crows were all sitting on the wire by the house. It's a sure sign that something awful is about to happen."

'Come on' I said. 'That's just an old wife's tale.'

'What d'you want me to do now Megan?'

'Bring him here to the Post Office. Doctor's here. We'll phone Mr Williams from here.'

I telephoned the number that Margaret Roderick had given me and got through to Mr Williams at home.

'Hello, Jim Williams speaking.'

'Hello Mr Williams, it's Brian Frost-Smith, I hope it's OK 'phoning you at home.'

'Oh sure. I was trying to contact Myfanwy Jenkins' husband to tell him the result of his wife's tests. I thought it right to talk to him first.'

'Yes I quite understand' said I, 'but apparently he's in a bit of a confused state with anxiety about his wife. He was found wandering down by the river. His family have seen him like this before and they are afraid of what he might do. Do you think you could tell me what you have found and the pathology report on the biopsy? If it is bad news I will be there with him to help.'

'Yes of course Brian. Well I am pleased to tell you that there is no bad news. At operation I found a uterus full of fibroids. The ovaries were normal, and I performed a hysterectomy. It was quite straight forward. The pathology lab reported that the biopsy did not contain any malignant cells. So that's all good news and I look forward to Myfanwy making a complete recovery. We gave her two pints of blood because her haemoglobin was only 70% of what it should have been. She's still on a saline drip, but she's back in the ward and wide awake. So her husband can come in to see her tonight for ten minutes if he would like to.'

'That's marvellous news,' I said. 'I'll tell him as soon as he appears'.

At that moment Dick came into the Post Office with Gwilym beside him looking deathly pale. He didn't say a word, he just collapsed into a chair with his head in his hands.

'Come on now Gwilym, I've got good news for you. Come on, sit up and listen.'

'Don't you be trying to soft soap me now,' said he.

'Listen Gwilym, Myfanwy is going to be alright. There is no cancer, d'you hear me, it's all good news'

Gwilym sat up and looked me straight in the face. 'You're not kidding me are you? It would be a cruel thing to do.'

'No, No, No! I'm not, I wouldn't think of such a thing! Mr Williams has been on the 'phone and spoken to me. He said that Myfanwy's operation was a complete success. She was very run down and they gave her some blood. She is now back in the ward and you can go in and see her for just ten minutes tonight.'

Gwilim's eyes filled with tears 'Diolch i Dduw!, Diolch i Dduw! (thank God! Thank God). Are you sure?' he asked again.

'You go now, to Powys ward in the infirmary and see for yourself.'

'You drive carefully, now Gwilym bach,' said Megan. 'We'll wait for you here and have a celebration drink when you get back.'

On Thursday afternoon I must call to see Dr Alun at home. He had just returned from London with his wife. So he will be back on duty for the practice from that evening. I rang the bell at Alun's house and went in. He was sitting in the lounge talking to his nephew.

'Hello, am I intruding?'

'No, no, come in' said he. 'David is just going to get me some cigarettes. Here you are David, will you get me twenty Players; here's the money, there's enough there, you can keep what's left.'

'Now Brian, how have you been getting on. Have there been any problems?'

'Not at all' said I. 'I've admitted one or two of your patients to hospital, and one or two I have referred to consultants at Aberystwyth. I'd better tell you about them so you are up to date.' We sat down. I had prepared a list of the most important of the patients I had seen. I went through it with him and told him particularly about Myfanwy Jenkins and mentioned how Gwilym had been so upset.

'Well it all resolved itself in the end; I think you did very well. Thank you very much for holding the fort. We had a lovely time in London; Kay spent a lot of money – so did I. But you know when you live in the depths of Wales, miles from any decent shops, it's like being let off the leash. And you see so many interesting things in the shops in Oxford Street you are tempted, and you have to put the brakes on!'

'Did you go to the Motor Show?' I asked.

'We did indeed and I was sorely tempted by the new models. But you know, they are all going for export. The new Austin A40 and the new Ford Zephyr are good models. I was told that there is a two years waiting list for all new cars. How did you like the Ford Prefect that you have been driving?'

'It's a very reliable car and it has behaved perfectly all the time.'

'Would you come again do you think if you were free one October time? It's very difficult for Kay and me to get away from a single handed practice for a holiday. I am afraid that it's difficult to get locums and I'm not too sure how any local arrangement with my nearest neighbour would work. I can't say that we mix with each other very well. The National Health Service is very new, and although we have had 'Panel Patients' for years, we haven't got used to the fact that everything is free now and that doctor's incomes depend entirely on how many patients they have registered with them.'

'Now you will want to get away. I've written a cheque for you for £35, is that sufficient?'

'Yes indeed, that is very generous if I may say so; and thank you for letting Marjorie and me stay at the Talbot Hotel. They have looked after us splendidly.'

'Marjorie is expecting the baby around the end of February. She has been very comfortable at The Talbot.'

'Well good luck Brian and thanks.'

We signed out at the hotel, made our way to the station and caught the six o'clock train to Caradog Falls Halt; the nearest point to my parents at Hafod.

4

WAR THREATENING

In the summer of 1938 we, as a family came to Wales for our summer holiday. My brother Hilary and I had already had a spring holiday by the sea, at Selsey following our incarceration in the Croydon Fever Hospital; not, I would admit, an experience I would like to repeat – ever! But I have to say that although a seaside holiday would have been envied by many children, especially having been loaned a really nice bungalow on the edge of the sandy beach, yet I could not compare the two holidays.

I loved the Welsh countryside, the hills, the farm around which I liked to wander and follow all that was going on. In fact that holiday I brought with me a device I had made with an old clock, an electric bell and a battery. It was set up to go off at six in the morning, and I didn't tell anyone what I was up to! My idea was that I wanted to see the very beginning of the day, and all that went on, on the farm from early morning. I got up quietly and crept outside. It was raining, that fine rain almost like a heavy mist, enough to dampen the enthusiasm of the keenest early riser. But I ran up the lane to Broncaradog, my uncle's farm, only to find my aunt and the maid servant Meg and the Gwas (the farm worker) called Dewi, all working hard doing the milking and all the chores that have to be done first thing in the morning. I was in fact disappointed. I remember well my feeling that no one wanted me around at that time of day.

In the summer months when there was a greater output of milk a large proportion would be put through the separator. The separator was a marvellous machine. As the milk entered, it was spun at just the right speed on the principle of the centrifuge. The skimmed milk came out of a large spout and the rich cream out of a small one. The skimmed milk was mixed with some meal and fed to the calves in a bucket while the eager calves tried to push their noses into the bucket in front of their fellows. Later, I would often do this job, standing with a bucket in each hand and

My grandfather, Edward Jones, who farmed at Ffosybleiddied.

trying to see that they all got a fair share! Turning the handle of the separator into which the milk was poured was quite hard, but that was a job that I did in later years; but in August of 1938, this was all new to me. I'd never been around at this hour before, and I have to say my enthusiasm for getting out of bed at six o'clock in the morning disappeared that day.

When I was very young, under six years old, I was not allowed to join my brother and cousin David and wander out after breakfast. To get to the farm, a road had to be crossed and no doubt Mother thought it would not be safe for me to do so. Actually, nearly all the traffic would be horse drawn; hardly any cars. I would be quite disappointed not to be allowed to join the two older boys who would run off laughing, ready for some adventure of which I wanted to be a part. I can remember that in an attempt to pacify me I was encouraged to sit on my grandfather's knee and smoke his pipe!

While the women were clearing the breakfast table, grandfather would sit by the fire. The tobacco he used was A1 Ringers Shag. This is a very strong tobacco with a very pungent smell. Believe it or not I was given one of his pipes, some of the tobacco was put in it and I attempted to light it. I cannot believe that I succeeded, it would surely have made me sick, but it definitely happened that way; the memory is very strong.

Grandfather, Edward Jones, was mother's father. She called him Papa and to us grandchildren he was Tad-gu, but every one pronounced it as if it were 'Tuckee'. He was, as I remember a gentle and friendly man aged at this time about 67. He had a large port wine birthmark called a haemangioma on the left side of his head. His birthplace was a village called Lledrod, nearby. He had married my grandmother, Jane, the eldest daughter of the family who lived in and farmed Ffosybleiddied. Dafydd

The old wool weaving mill in the village. It was more than a little derelict but we put a corrugated iron roof on it, a window and a door to render it weatherproof.

Meredith, my great, great, great, great grandfather came to this farm with his wife Catherine around 1750 from Llanfihangel Genaur Glyn, a village just a few miles north of Aberystwyth and so Mother was his great, great, great grand daughter.

For us, as a family, summer holidays in this rather remote cottage, Trefriwfach was a complete change. My grandfather was widowed around 1928, and then he lived with his housekeeper, her name was Jane but for some reason she was called Jane-o. This was the situation there as far back as I can remember. Before that, the summer holiday was spent at Ffosybleiddied mother's family home and birthplace; I don't remember those days.

When on holiday there in Trefriwfach, in my grandfather's time, we were looked after by his housekeeper, so life was relatively easy. The fact that the cottage had no modern facilities: electric light, water and flush toilets, had limited impact on us: after all we were only there for a few weeks. But it became more like a camping holiday after grandfather's death: for the next three holidays 1936 to 1938 inclusive we had to look after ourselves: no resident house keeper but mother had some daily help: Mr and Mrs James 'The Hut' which was a small cottage abut a mile down the railway line and on the edge of the line.

In 1937, I could see that Father was up to something. While we were on holiday some very large rolls of electric cable, some electric meters and a big dynamo arrived. These were all redundant items from the local power station at Aberystwyth. The 'Grid System' had arrived in Aber' and these were being sold off at give away prices. Electricity was not going to extend out to the country areas for some years and I could see what father was planning!

In the village of Tynygraig there was an old weaving factory. The roof was missing but we put on a corrugated iron replacement. Most of the walls were in good repair, and when we added a new window and door, it was fit to install the equipment to   provide electricity. There was a water wheel pit and the power from this had been used to drive the weaving and carding machines, the remains of which were still there.

There was some good mahogany in the frames of the looms that had otherwise collapsed into rusting heaps. The only memento that I have now of that place is a small mahogany box that I made when I was sixteen to take a miniature set of chess men made out of old ebony round ruler and bone knitting needles; these chess men I had turned up on the lathe. My uncle Tom of Broncaradog told me that when he was a boy in the 1850s, they had weavers, a fuller, a tanner, a cobbler and a tailor in the village. He said that one could be fitted out with clothes and footwear without leaving the village.

There was also a Flour Mill to grind corn to make bread. The remains of that was there down by the railway halt. The two sisters, the 'Miss Laurie's the Mill' lived there and later during the war, I would pass them every day when going for the train to take me to school.

So this was Father's plan: to re-install a water wheel to drive the dynamo to make electric light for Trefriwfach. The water race still entered the factory and flowed down to the water wheel pit. He recruited helpers, but the one I knew best was Jack Roderick. He was a bachelor living on his own and he was full of wise sayings. He was the handyman of the village; he could make or repair almost anything that would be used on the farm. He could also slaughter and butcher a pig or lamb and did so regularly for my aunt when it was that time of year.

The scheme was to purchase a six foot diameter split pulley with a flat face onto which could be bolted elevator buckets. Wooden sides were bolted to the buckets to make a water wheel. Most of the necessary bits and pieces could be found at the old lead mining sites that were scattered locally along the River Ystwyth.

In 1938 the water wheel was built and installed in the old woollen factory, together with counter shafting and the old direct current dynamo driven by belt, to produce a 230 volt supply of electricity for the cottage.

The posts and cable were installed when I was still at home in South Croydon and at school in the summer term of 1938, so that by the time we arrived on holiday the power was there in the house. The biggest snag of the whole scheme was that the amount of water available to turn the wheel was sometimes limited. If it ever dried up, the light would go out and it would be back to candles again! Fortunately that happened mostly in the summer and during the war we had double daylight saving, so the clocks were forwarded two hours!

This was Father's second attempt to make electric light and was only partially effective. He was not to be put off; later when we moved to Hafod he had another attempt!

Many people called 1938 the crisis year. Hitler was demanding the part of Czechoslovakia bordering on Germany on the grounds that most people living there were ethnic Germans. He called it Sudetenland. Prime Minister Chamberlain and the leaders of France and Italy agreed providing that there were fifty per cent of Germans in the parts he wanted to annex. In September that year, at Munich, Hitler said he wanted all of that part of Czechoslovakia regardless of the percentage of Germans living there. He said that this was the last of his territorial demands. Britain, France and Italy agreed and signed the agreement at the end of September 1938. Chamberlain came back to Britain waving the agreement paper and saying: 'Peace in our time'. The newspaper's headlines, I remember: 'Have no fear, there will be no war!'

At the end of the holiday we went back home to South Croydon, and I, to Whitgift School. In the summer of 1939, while we were on our usual summer holiday in Wales Hitler invaded Poland and, refused to remove his troops from there. We declared war against Germany on 3 September 1939. I remember clearly that no one I came across seemed unduly alarmed. 'It'll be over by Christmas,' people were saying, just as they said in 1915!

The advent of war changed my life completely: changed it for the better without any doubt! I was told that I would be attending school in Aberystwyth. I took it in my stride, and we all went to see the Head-master, Mr D. C. Lewis. He showed us around Ardwyn County School. I liked what I saw; it looked friendly and homely. On the other hand Hilary, who had set his sights on Cambridge University and a career as an engineer, felt that the laboratory set up was not as good as it was at Whitgift. He needed good examination results. He needn't have worried: he did very well, but worked hard to get there. As for me, I revelled in the fact that I was now permanently living in my beloved Wales.

We had always spent every summer holiday at my grandfather's cottage called Trefriwfach, in the very small village Tynygraig, near Ystrad Meurig. My mother was a native of Swyddffynnon, another small village nearby and so I was already half Welsh. When the war started we simply stayed on in the cottage which we had kept for holidays though by that time my grandfather was dead. Of course it was a little strange, this move to a new school in Wales. I had previously attended Whitgift which was a public school for day boys. It was immediately obvious that this was going to be a quite different sort of school; the whole atmosphere was different. There was a feeling of warmth and friendliness compared with the strict and rather harsh discipline at Whitgift. Anyone who has attended an English public school will know what I mean.

All pupils in my year had to decide at this point, entering fourth form, whether to join the language, the modern or the science group in preparation for the School Certificate examination or Senior as it was called. Though I was never a particularly bright student, I had quite decided to go in for science and so I joined 'Form 4L', Mr Lloyd's form. He was the chemistry teacher and a very nice man he was too; as were all the teachers with whom I came into contact; there was a feeling of caring throughout the school, a friendliness I had not been used to; not an atmosphere of fear.

I remember at the end of the first week on Friday afternoon at the end of school I said to some small lad with whom I had struck up an instant friendship 'See you tomorrow'. In Whitgift, as in many schools, pupils had to attend school on Saturday morning; Saturday afternoon was devoted to games. As far as I was concerned, that meant school all day Saturday! 'What do you mean?' he said – 'No school on Saturdays!' My heart leapt with joy!

We, my brother and I, travelled to school on the train that arrived at Caradog Falls Halt from Carmarthen. This was scheduled to arrive at the Halt at about eight o'clock, and indeed it did for most of the first term, getting us to school in good time. As the war progressed however and the bombing started in London, the Carmarthen train would arrive late at our halt, any time between half past nine and eleven o'clock. This was because it had to wait in Carmarthen for the London connection. There was no way of finding out just how late the train was going to be, we had to wait in the meagre shelter of the halt which was just a shack, until the train arrived!

This meant we were regularly late, arriving at school around eleven thirty, or even later in the morning. Educationally this was a disaster for me. My school work, never excellent, accordingly deteriorated. In the school terminal and annual exams we were classed with grade one to grade four, according to the marks obtained in each subject, grade one being very good and grade four a fail! My average was always in the region of 2.6 which meant an average of about three – just a pass, no more. My brother rebelled and insisted on going into 'digs' or lodgings in Aberystwyth so that he would be at school on time.

He was working for Higher School Certificate and so it was considered to be more important for him than for me. Incidentally he was always called Edward at Ardwyn because being a co-ed school any pupil called Hilary would be a girl! So he was naturally a little embarrassed to be called Hilary although it was the name he used throughout his life apart from his time at Ardwyn. He went on to Cambridge – Peterhouse – and read engineering later being appointed Professor of Electrical Engineering at Queen's University Belfast. Sadly he died in 1978 at the age of 54. He had two sons, only one of whom is alive and living in France.

The next year, fifth form I was ill so much of the year that I did not attempt School Certificate. I dropped back a year and left some of my friends behind. I fell in with new fifth form friends and started living in digs so that at least I could be in time for school.

It was very quiet in Aberystwyth during that time of war, very few cars, no One Way streets and no traffic lights. If you were lucky enough to come into town in a car, you could park on any street anywhere, anywhere at all!

Like most people who lived out in the countryside, our cottage had no running water, drainage system or mains electricity so candles were often used for light, if the water wheel was not working. The loo was Ty Bach (small house) at the bottom of the garden, with a bucket and disinfectant that had to be emptied. Father had installed the water powered electricity by the end of 1938, but we still had no drinking water laid on in the cottage.

One of my chores was to carry water twice a day from the 'Pistyll' (pure water coming out of the rock) in two buckets full, up to the house about 400 yards from down in the Cwm, the wooded valley below our cottage. I tried to think of all possible ways to get water pumped up to the house but in the end I decided to get permission to dig a well near the house. I persuaded a water diviner to come from Llanafan, a village about three miles away. He chose the best spot just behind the house where he reckoned two underground channels of water flowing in the limestone joined together.

My mother asked Tommy Roderick of Talfryn, a younger brother of Jack who had helped us with the electricity installation. Tommy had been a lead miner and came to do the work. This is where it all sounds a little odd, but nevertheless it is all quite true! I was the helper and when we had dug a hole about four feet down and six feet diameter we hit rock. 'We will have to blast with gelignite' he said. He gave me instructions on what to buy: gelignite, detonators and fuse and off I went to Tom Old, the farm supply shop in Baker Street.

'You must get a letter from your headmaster to say you are competent' he said. In today's world, just imagine a boy of sixteen asking his headmaster for a letter giving him permission to buy explosives! But that is exactly what I did; and he gave me the letter. Good Old Chest (Headmaster D. C. Lewis) he must have trusted me.

I bought the explosives and Tommy brought the chisels to cut holes twelve inches deep into the rock. I sometimes think of myself then, crouching down in a deep hole holding the chisel while Tommy belted it with a sledge hammer and I had to turn it a little after each blow. The powdered rock was removed every so often with a tool designed for that purpose. Tommy having been a lead miner all his life owned the necessary tools and was an expert. When the holes were deep enough, the gelignite with the detonator and fuse were inserted into the holes and soil or sand packed in on top. The ladder was in place and I scrambled out; Tommy lit the fuse, he was as cool as a cucumber. Then he hurried up after me. We both retreated to a safe distance and waited for the big Bang! All the rock and debris had to be removed bucket full by bucket full using a rope and pulley fixed on a crossbar above the hole.

I was worried after two or three of these detonations. What, I said to myself, would happen if Tommy stumbled on the ladder and was unable to climb out before the detonation? I went back to Mr Old and asked if there was such a thing as an electric detonator. I had seen these being used on the films. 'Yes,' he said and supplied me with more detonators this time with two feet of wire attached. Detonators are extremely sensitive, containing mercury fulminate. I tried one out: I attached an extension, an extra long length of wire and placed the detonator behind a wall and with myself in a safe position, I touched the ends of the wires on a battery. Bang! it worked and safely too! It was extraordinary that Tommy was so composed and cool lighting the fuse and hurriedly climbing out of the hole; he had of course been used to doing it as a lead miner. But when it came to putting the electric detonator in its place his hands shook and he was very quiet, obviously nervous. It was of course essential to keep the battery some way away to avoid accidentally switching on at the wrong time.

He told me that when he worked in the lead mines near a village called Ponterwyd, a matter of about ten to fifteen miles from his home, he was blasting rock like this almost every day. At the end of each day, the foreman called out: 'Put it on the nail and show the candle.' He was instructing the man to put the end of the long tape measure on the base of the pit; the foreman up on the edge of the hole measured the amount that the miners had excavated down and they were paid accordingly. Tommy walked to work and back home every day.

We blasted the rock and cleared the debris out on to a pile out of the way. Eventually when we reached a depth of about fourteen feet, water began to seep in from the sides of the well and we had increasing difficulty in working in the wet. We managed to achieve a depth of about eighteen feet and water was now coming in quite fast so we stopped digging. The rest was easy. With a semi-rotary pump from M. H. Davies the ironmonger in Bridge Street and galvanised water pipe, it would seem that the problem of domestic drinking water was solved. We covered the well with some substantial wooden planking and put a simple fence around the hole in the ground for safety, and that seemed to be that – problem solved!

It was not to be so... At the end of the summer Father came home for a holiday to Trefriwfach. At the start of the war he had been moved from South London to Wales to cope with the influx of evacuees in the primary schools. As HMI he then visited schools in the area of Llandovery and schools in Breconshire. But when the major bombing of London and the South East stopped with the defeat of the German air force at the end of the Battle of Britain, most of the children returned home.

He was now posted back to the South East to resume school inspection in that area. I think he was not sorry to move back. He was not Welsh speaking and sometimes felt a little alien in that part of Wales. His home had been in Essex.

On his first day back at home in Trefriwfach, I told him all about my work with Tommy, digging the well. He was very interested; we always got on well with each other, working together on any project. So at lunchtime he said, 'Let me try a glass of water from our new well. That's a queer smell,' he said as he lifted the glass to his lips. I sniffed the water in his glass.

'Oh my God, it's foul,' said I in disgust. 'There's something terribly wrong. Don't drink it!' We could hardly wait until lunch was over before we lifted the wooden cover off the well. We could detect the foul smell at once. We took a sample in a clean bottle to the Milk Marketing Laboratory in Aberystwyth.

They were very helpful, and the very next day sent their report on the bacteriology of the sample: 'There is an unacceptable count of B.Coli (balantidium coli) in the water.' They gave the figures. This organism is a trophozoite which occurs in the digestive tract of some mammals. It is the only protozoan that infects humans. We pumped all the water out of the well and I climbed down to inspect. There at the bottom were the decomposing remains of several small animals, moles and mice that had burrowed in through the soil and then tumbled into the water.

It was a long, hard job. I removed the animal remains and then scrubbed the rocky walls of the well with disinfectant very thoroughly. We constructed a panel of wood and fixed it firmly to the top of the rock so that any creature popping out of the soil would not fall in the water but remain on the cover. Then we filled and emptied the well using the pump several times. The whole exercise took about a week working on and off. We sent a sample to the laboratory and the report came back stating that the water was now pure and fit to drink.

That all happened in 1942 when I was sixteen, and during the summer holidays. We left Trefriwfach in 1945 and moved to a large house called Hafod that was empty and belonged to a relative. At this point my uncle and aunt retired from their farm, Broncaradog and moved into Trefriwfach. They continued to use the well until about 1952 when mains water came to the area. The well was then closed down.

As a family we spent the six years of the war in this rather remote part of west Wales, ten miles south west of Aberystwyth. The most exciting thing that happened in the winter was the deep snow that covered the hedges and the gates so that, as I had been told when on holiday, we would walk over these boundaries. In the summer, we were very conscious of the harvest and the importance of getting hay and corn dry and under cover. It was sublimely peaceful. On the numerous occasions in the winter of 1941, when I lay in bed ill, all I would hear through the bedroom window facing the Cwm would be the sound of the river at the bottom of the valley, and the song of the birds; especially the owls at night. There was no sound of aeroplanes or cars or tractors. All the work on the farms around was done with horses.

When I was sixteen in the summer of 1942 I was persuaded to help with the corn harvest. The reaping machine had sharp triangular cutters moving rapidly with a reciprocating motion and was pulled by two horses. That was straight forward. If the weather was fine, and after two Sundays had passed; not two weeks, as the old saying instructed, the hay was gathered into manageable rows by a horse drawn rake. This, as I remember was a new machine in the early 1930s. Before that, the hay was raked by hand into rows. When quite dry it was brought in, pitched with two pronged pitch forks onto a 'Gambo' (a two wheeled dray) and stored in the hay lofts above the stables and cowsheds. All ready to be fed to the animals in the winter. Nowhere in that area did I ever see a baler!

The corn harvest was different: the same reaping machine was used but there were two seats on it. My uncle sat on the one on the side nearest the cutters and wielded a foot pedal that, could elevate a hinged rack that would catch enough of the cut corn to make a sheaf. When the rack was lowered the bundle of corn would be left behind on the ground to be bound into a sheaf using a few strands of the corn itself. There would be a number of helpers, some from the village following the reaper and binding the sheaves. The whole process was very labour intensive.

My job in the corn cutting was to drive the reaper, guiding the horses who obviously knew very well what they had to do and which way they had to go! We only cut one way; at the end of the row I would turn the horses, go back and start cutting another row. If I, my cousin or my brother were not available, then the farm worker would have to step in. But that was a waste of his valuable expertise. Driving the horses was a simple unskilled job and I could do that well enough!

Tea in the corn field was very pleasurable eating my aunt's home-made bread and home-made butter. Seeing the bound sheaves all around as a testimony to our hard work. It was an unpaid job but I was very much aware of the hospitality of my aunt who fed me plentifully when ever I appeared at a meal time!

We were sheltered from the savagery of the war that was going on all around the world. We were only partly aware of it. We listened to the nine o'clock news on the antiquated radio we had. We even listened to Lord Haw Haw! That was a joke! Altogether I think we realised that the news reporting the number of German planes shot down was optimistic and that our losses were correspondingly played down. But we did not realise perhaps how close our country was to defeat, especially in the war against the German U boats in the Atlantic.

One afternoon, I remember Mr Tom Owen came to tea in Trefriwfach. He was an HMI colleague of my father and I was friendly with his son. He had served in the 1914 to 1918 war in the Royal Flying Corps. He told us how he had flown over enemy lines in his bi-plane gathering information on troop movements and occasionally firing at enemy soldiers with his revolver – that was the only gun he had! But Mr Owen knew from his experience of how the war was progressing; with the Germans occupying almost all of Europe, gaining ground wherever their armies attacked. And there was the threat ever present that if they could gain air superiority there would be an invasion of England. Nobody of course knew then, when the Germans were intending to attack Russia.

Someone at the tea table asked Tom Owen if he thought we would win the war against Germany. I remember feeling a little surprised and anxious, as I think the others there were at his answer: 'My patriotism' he said 'tells me that we can't possibly lose the war, but my intelligence tells me that I cannot see how we can possibly win!'

We were living in a very peaceful part of the British Isles. Life in that part of Wales carried on as usual. There were none of the sounds or sights of war, no soldiers in uniform, no aeroplanes, bombing or gunfire.

The rural scene was entirely calm and peaceful as far as the eye could see. The only sounds coming to the ears were the sounds generated by nature: bird song , the occasional neighing of a horse or other animal sounds. On the other hand there were a number of rules we had to obey. We had to cover our windows with blinds so that no light could be seen from outside the house at night. Cars had to have their headlights partly covered and street lighting in the local towns was very dim; if present at all. The chiming of church bells was prohibited. We were told that if there was an invasion by German forces, church bells throughout the land would ring out.

There was food rationing. We were all issued with Identity Cards and Ration Books. Food rationing had much less effect on country dwellers than those living in large towns. I do not know what the regulations were when it came to slaughtering a pig. At Broncaradog, my uncle's farm, the pig was killed in the early part of every year. It was butchered on the farm and preserved by traditional methods using mainly salt. The hams and legs were hung from the kitchen ceiling by hooks. Almost every day at Broncaradog the midday meal was boiled ham, potatoes, cabbage and butter, followed by rice pudding. As a young boy, this was not my favourite meal! At the weekend, Sunday lunch would be roast chicken. The result was that the general public in villages in a farming area sometimes were allowed more meat than the rather limited ration allowed for town dwellers. There was also the Black Market, prevalent I believe in the bigger towns and cities; but we were really not aware of it where we lived.

By the end of 1942 I had tried my Central Welsh Board School Certificate and had gained the five credits I needed to obtain the Matriculation Certificate. This was necessary in order to gain a place at most universities at that time.

It was too late to register at Aberystwyth University for the academic year commencing October 1942, and I had not really decided just what course I wanted to follow. I toyed with the idea of going into the teaching profession. My parents did their best to dissuade me from that, having both served as school teachers at Appleby Grammar School. I didn't quite understand, then, why they thought that was not a good plan for me. I must say I do understand now! Then I seriously considered the

Church as a vocation. I was a keen attender at Gwnnws, our local church on the hill. The notion of preaching my 'way out' ideas to a captive audience appealed to me – never mind whether it was consistent with Church thought.

I was just sixteen years old and full of immature ideals. I soon gave all that up. I was very interested in all of the science I had studied, particularly biology. Hilary was in the middle of his degree course in engineering at Cambridge. I saw at close quarters the work he was coping with. The mathematics was obviously too difficult for my poor brain! But I liked the practical aspects of work as an engineer: I was a practical person, but that is not enough.

My cousin David, the one who gave me scarlet fever in 1936, was in his second year of Medicine at the Welsh National School of Medicine at Cardiff. I was fascinated by what he was doing, studying human anatomy and physiology. Now that appealed to me. I stayed at school that year filling in my time learning some more biology and some physics.

During the war, once you reached the age of eighteen, unless you were in the middle of a course of study, 'Call Up' papers would arrive. I decided, having the bare necessary credits in subjects that would give me Matriculation that I would enter Aberystwyth University as a first year medical student. That was October 1943. So in September of 1943, I made my way up to the Registrar's Office in the main college building by the castle.

I had sent the Registrar my certificates and asked him if I could enter the University College as a first year student to take the first MB course. I had received a letter telling me to attend at the Office on a specific date. There were a number of admission clerks sitting at desks to interview applicants for the October entry that year. I approached one of them and handed her my appointment letter. She looked at the letter, and then at me.

'Ah, Mr Frost-Smith' she said. I looked around expecting to see my father. That was the first time that I had been addressed with a 'Mr'. I was always called 'Frost-Smith minor' at Whitgift; 'Brian' at Ardwyn, and mostly Frost or Frosty to my friends. The admissions clerk gave me information, leaflets and instructions on how to proceed next, and away

I went; fully enrolled as a first year student – as easy as that!

I soon met up with quite a number of my friends, three at least entering the same course as I, and a few entering the first year of pure science degree courses. It was a very 'chummy' set up! As I remember, there were only about 500 students in the college so it was a very friendly environment. The course was called intermediate, which was the name for the first year of a degree course. I did 'Inter' in four subjects: zoology, botany, chemistry and physics, the pre-med course in preparation to enter the Welsh National School of Medicine at Cardiff.

I really enjoyed that year at Aber Coll as it was called. It was unusual: firstly because the frequent meetings of the various college societies, whether it was the Chemistry Society or maybe the Geographical Society, they were attended by huge crowds of the students, quite apart from whether they had an interest in the subject. It was a great 'get together'. After all, there was little entertainment going on in the town. The Pier had closed, I think even the Coliseum Cinema had shut. The college refectory, new, having been built in the 1930s had been taken over by the RAF who were stationed in the town. So students met frequently in the examination hall and were entertained by members of the music department. We also sang hymns; mostly Welsh hymns! The College Song had been composed when the college came into being in the late nineteenth century. I knew it well because Mother used to sing it often, to remind her of old and happy days!

Some boast their classic stream
Where Nymphs and Naiads dream,
Their buildings touched by time till old and grey.
Our college towers in pride, by the western waters wide,
Where wild waves vainly beat along the bay.

What may your motto be, O college by the sea?
Nid Byd Byd Heb Wybodaeth answer we.
(Life without knowledge is no life at all)
Rage ye gales ye surges seethe Aberystwyth fu a fydd.
                                        (live for ever)
From near or distant home, her sons and daughters come,
Awhile to tarry by the wind swept shore,

129

Dim midnight oil they burn, nor sport and pleasure spurn.
Those days shall dwell in mem'ry evermore

What may your motto be, O college by the sea, etc.

We did not sing that emotive song at all! Instead we sang:

For we come here to learn, midnight oil lamps to burn
Up in Aber, Aber, Aber, up in Aber
But before very long, it's wine women and song,
Up in Aber, Aber, Aber, up in Aber.
Bangor Cardiff Swansea know us of old,
When we're up against them, we leave them cold!
So there's one place for me, that's the Coll' by the sea,
Up in Aber, Aber, Aber, up in Aber.

Most of the student lived in lodgings or digs and only a few lived at home in the town. These were the ones that I knew best, having been at school with them. I would have to find digs, because although the Carmarthen to Aberystwyth train now ran more or less on time I would miss out on college life if I did not live in the town. We found a suitable landlady, Mrs Price at Nuneham, North Road, who already had one student resident. He was a Czechoslovakian Jew and his name was George Ader.

He and his mother had escaped the German persecution of the Jews in Czechoslovakia and had arrived in London where he, a clever young man had entered London University to read for an Honours Degree in Chemistry. During the war the whole of the London University Chemistry Department was removed to Aberystwyth. So he and I were to live in this house for a year, while he completed his degree and I finished my one year first MB course. We shared our living room, we shared our bedroom, we even shared our bed! Washing was jug and basin.

The female students, except those that lived at home, lived in the Women's Halls of Residence; Alexander Hall situated at the end of the Promenade and Carpenter Hall nearby. Only the postgraduate female students lived in approved digs; even they, mature women students, were subject to rules and regulations as to how and when they could go out and what time they had to return to the lodging. The male students were not restricted in any way and there were no halls of residence for men.

Cafés and restaurants were only allowed to charge a maximum of five shillings for a meal served to customers. Most ordinary casual lunch menus would cost about one or two shillings (5-10p). Male students could join the college dining club that served a simple midday or evening meal cheaply. Students had to opt for one or the other, but in fact Freshers like me, would have to accept the later meal which was not so popular because it interfered with work and activities at that time. I quite enjoyed having my main meal in this way, and as a diversion we invited a guest speaker occasionally. On one occasion the club invited George Bernard Shaw to come and talk to us. We got a short, sharp reply: 'Where and what is Aberystwyth?'

I found the first MB course very interesting and engaging: All the lecturers in the four subjects I was required to study were excellent teachers who made a point of being friendly and helpful. I enjoyed particularly the practical work. In practical botany I sat next to a tall red headed girl called Gaynor. She looked at me rather disapprovingly; I must admit I was rather a scruffy lad. Bathroom facilities in Trefriwfach were primitive; no bath or shower, so perhaps I even smelled a little like a farmyard!

She spoke with a marked South Wales sing song accent: 'What you goyin' to do next year then?' she asked.

'I'm going to Cardiff to the Medical School' said I. She gave a derisive laugh!

'And what makes you think you'll get in there then? I tried to get in, but they wouldn't 'ave me see.' I wonder why, thought I.

The next week I was summoned to see Professor Lily Newton. She was professor of botany and an imposing dignified lady. She was also on the selection board for entry to Cardiff Medical School. I went up to her office and knocked.

'Come in' she called out cheerfully. I entered.

'Now Mr Frost-Smith, I think you have to attend at the admission selection board in Cardiff next week.' I was a little anxious, what was she going to say.

'Now look here' she said, 'remember you have to make a good impression on the board. You must see that you are tidily dressed and with a clean shirt.'

'I'll do my best' I said.

'Good luck' said she, and that was all!

So at the end of the academic year I passed the exams and prepared to move to Cardiff as a second year Med. This was the first time I had lived away from home, and I, like many students was still a little immature. The first time I ever went into a pub to have drink before plucking up courage to attend a student dance in the King's Hall, I wasn't quite sure how to order. I said to the barmaid: 'Can I have a half pint of beer please?'

She replied: 'Sorry we've only got IPA.'

I really didn't know what IPA was, but I took the plunge.

'Okay that'll do thanks.' I had only ever gone into a pub with Father, and I had never tasted beer before! That was just the beginning!

5

MEDICAL SCHOOL AT CARDIFF

I attended the admissions interview. I cannot remember who was on the board; I didn't know any of them anyway. They looked me up and down and verified my name and age. They did not enquire about my qualifications to enter, which is just as well! The only question I remember, one of them asking me was: Did I want to be a surgeon or a physician. I was alright on that subject, but I'll have to be careful what I say. I remembered the old joke: 'Surgeons do everything and know nothing! Physicians know everything but do nothing! Psychiatrists know nothing and do nothing!'

I giggled inwardly! What I actually answered, was something like this: 'I won't be able to decide what I want to do until I have had more experience of what is involved. I do like working in close contact with people, and I think of myself in General Practice from what I've seen.'

'Very good my boy, thank you that is all. You can go now,' said the chairman of the board.

A few days before the first day of term I made my way on the train to Cardiff and was met by my cousin David. He had located suitable digs for me at number Nine Column Road about a mile from the Medical School. Mrs Edwards was the landlady. She was a warm homely woman, and she showed me up to my room. It was luxurious compared to my digs in Aberystwyth. She was very hospitable; typical in fact of South Wales people. It was quite common for students then to live in lodgings that provided meals. I would have my lunch in the college refectory but all the other meals in my digs. Mrs Edwards looked after us and fed us well. I shared the accommodation with three others. There was Dai Rowlands a sixth year Med. He was a little late passing his final clinical exams. He qualified the next year I believe. There was also a young lad who worked at the Tredegar Trading Estate, and a Women's Auxiliary Air Force (WAAF) called Tommy. It was a very happy set up

133

and we got on well together.

I had completed my first year at Aberystwyth, where the work was devoted entirely to pure science. Now I was about to embark on the next two years in which I would be studying normal human science: anatomy, physiology, pharmacology, organic chemistry and an extra subject, not normally part of a medical curriculum: anthropology. We were called: preclinical students because we never entered a hospital or engaged in the study of disease processes. That would come in the last three years of our study.

Most of our work during the day was spent in the dissecting room learning human anatomy, learning in detail the normal structure of the body. It was the most difficult part of the two year course and we had to complete it successfully and pass tests at intervals before an examination at the end of the year, and the final examination at the end of the two year course. We were expected to learn in great detail and be able to describe the structures of the human body and their relationships to each other. We had regular lectures on the most difficult and important areas of the body, especially those that had a direct relationship with surgery.

In order that we had a clear three dimensional image of all this, we had to actually dissect out and identify the parts of the body in a particular region. It was well arranged. After we, my partner and I had completed dissecting an area and exposed and identified the important structures in it, we had to pass an informal oral test: a *viva voce*. There were many demonstrators in the room, all being fairly newly qualified doctors re-learning their anatomy in preparation to take a further examination. We would ask one of them to conduct the test: it was quite informal but our test card had to be signed. One of the demonstrators turned out to be John Parry. His father was my mother's first cousin. He was very helpful and friendly.

Before I started this course I used to bite my finger nails. I soon stopped! We did not wear gloves when dissecting human tissue as I believe students do today. The washing facilities were excellent, but the thought of my eating bits of the corpse was enough to cure me of the habit of nail biting permanently.

The cadavers to be dissected were lying on oblong tables in the dissecting room. At first sight, being covered up with brown sheets, they looked just like brown oblong bundles. I must confess, I was very curious to see what a dead body looked like! When one was partially uncovered, I was surprised to see that it did not look like a dead person, or what I had imagined a dead person would look like. They were somehow shrunk and shrivelled which in a way de-humanised them. They smelled strongly of formalin.

Professor West told us that we must behave with absolute respect; these were once human beings who had freely donated their bodies to aid the advance of medical knowledge. He said that when the dissecting process was finished, the corpse and all the body parts that had been temporarily removed for examination, would be put decently together and respectfully interred. He was very emphatic about this and I am glad to say that his instructions were respected by all of us.

I and many of my friends found it extremely difficult to assimilate and remember the vast number of facts involved, we knew we were going to be tested frequently, and that helped, but we had to gather all the facts together and be ready to sit the final examination at the end of the second year before being allowed to move on to fourth year. This was, for me the biggest hurdle that I had to overcome in the entire medical course. It was a long string of facts that just had to be memorised and it was helpful to have a visual memory. Combined with pure anatomy we studied embryology: the development of the embryo as a whole and of the major organs to maturity. We also studied histology when we sat at a bench looking down a microscope and trying to identify various important cells and tissues of the body. We learned to cut wafer thin sections of tissues with a microtome and stain and mount them on a glass microscope slide.

I am glad to say, and I believe that I am correct, that today's anatomy student in the medical course concentrates mainly on the most important areas of the human body that are relevant to disease processes. Several of the more enterprising students over the years made up mnemonics as an aid to memory. I used to know many of them but I only remember one or two now.

There is one about the lingual nerve: The Lingual nerve is a branch of the fifth cranial nerve. It is important in dentistry because a local anaesthetic given to block pain when extracting a wisdom tooth can damage it. This would result in some loss of sensation and taste perception in the tongue. Some 'wag' thought it important to recognise the course of this nerve in the neck: 'The lingual nerve, it takes a swerve around the hyoglossus. Well I'll be f... d said Wharton's duct, the bugger's double crossed us!'

It does go more or less round the hyoglossus muscle that links the hyoid bone (Adam's apple) to the tongue, and Whartons duct is one of the salivary excretion ducts. I suppose it could be important to know just where it is in the mouth!

Human physiology, the normal functioning of the body was another very important subject we studied in the second and third year of the course. I think we all found it easier to take in than anatomy. Of course, much more about human physiology is known today than was known then. We attended practical sessions in which we investigated beating frogs' hearts and the mechanism of muscular contraction, as well as blood chemistry and the physiology of nerve function.

We had lectures on pharmacology which then, was a comparatively small subject. Most drugs in use were alkaloids, extracted from plants like *digitalis* from the foxglove, morphine from the poppy and *belladonna* from deadly nightshade. The synthetic production of drugs had not really got off the ground. The study of cortisone and the structure and use of hormones was only just beginning. For example: The specific treatment for Addison's disease in which the adrenal glands which sit on top of the kidneys fail to produce their hormone was untreatable except by supportive measures.

If you were born with it you did not survive many years. The discovery of cortisone and related substances changed all that.

I was very happy with my life as a second year medical student. My digs were very comfortable, I made a lot of new friends and I enjoyed the social life. In my first week, I was asked if I was going to the 'smoker' that evening. 'What is a smoker?' I asked. I remember it well! It was a kind of drunken orgy held in the upper room of the pub on the corner of Queen's Street. Quite a large number of medical students were there, but it was very sexist: no women! I think women medical students could have come, but wisely they gave it a miss. There were large

wooden barrels of beer and we all drank pint after pint and smoked cigarette after cigarette, until the room was a haze of swaying bodies in the
smoke. It was the first but not the last time for me until I learned more
sense!

During that year I caught mumps and had to go home for two or three
weeks. It kept me out of trouble however, and I was very lucky in that
my working partner Paul, who was a very bright young man, sent me
all the notes from the physiology lectures that I was missing, and which
were so important. I was able to copy them up and it kept me busy and
up to date with what was going on.

Meanwhile, my cousin David was in his fifth year and was living in
the Medical Students Club in Howard Gardens very near the Infirmary
and right in the centre of life in the Medical School. It was a very desirable place in which to live, but there were no pre-clinical residents,
mainly because there was a waiting list to enter, and in nearly every case,
by the time you got into the club you would be in fourth year or above.
Suddenly David's friend, who shared his double room, left and went to
Morriston Hospital as a student doctor to help with the big influx of
wounded service men.

I was lucky! David asked me if I would like to join him and share
his room. I was delighted and moved from Column Road into the club.
The rent was the same as it had been in my digs. All meals except for
lunch were provided. Lunch was available but you had to pay for that
separately. It was much nearer the anatomy and physiology departments.
It was altogether more convenient and I got to know many more students. The next year, my third year and David's sixth year, I had to con-
centrate on revising for the second MB exams that would be in June.

David left the club sometime in February and went to join his friend
in Morriston Hospital as a student doctor. That left me with a space to
fill and I asked Sam Mitchel, a school friend to join me. He jumped at
the idea and was delighted. He was a year ahead of me and had been
chosen by an election to be secretary of the Medical Students Club. At
the end of the year I managed, not without some difficulty, to pass the
examinations in the pre-clinical subjects.

This gave me a BSc degree and was the passport to enter the fourth
year of study. It was a big step forward: I would now spend much of

my time in the teaching hospital: Cardiff Royal Infirmary. I would receive teaching and clinical demonstrations from consultants and professors in the different specialities. First of all I had to be kitted out: Two short white jackets that had to be kept scrupulously clean! A skin pencil, a tape measure, a patellar hammer for testing reflexes and a stethoscope. Armed with these, and in the company of five or six students like myself, I made my way up to William Diamond Ward where we were met by the Professor of Medicine, Jock Kennedy.

He was a stern but kind man, and when, on his ward round, you had to stand up straight, no slouching and speak only if spoken to. He taught us how to take a history from patients and how to examine them. There was little talk of special laboratory tests or X rays. In fact I was told that he charged his junior staff a shilling for each X ray they ordered that he considered unnecessary! X rays and laboratory tests were a new feature and not common in his younger days. He said in his marked Scots accent: 'If ye're up in the Highlands or in the outer Isles, ye'll not have anything like that to help ye.'

So he taught us the first basic rules when attending a patient: history; inspection; palpation and percussion and auscultation. He made us practice it on live and long-suffering patients. The patients we examined in nearly all the departments would become National Health patients. Some patients contributed to a scheme like Penny in the Pound, and that covered the cost of hospitalisation before 1948 when the National Health Service started.

Students were divided into groups and attached to a 'firm', a consultant or a senior medic with their junior staff. They, the students would follow the consultant and his team around the ward and the outpatient clinics where some patients would be the focus of attention and would be used to illustrate the points on which the consultant was teaching. It was usually explained to a patient that these were young doctors in training. A little later on, individual students in a consultant's team would be allocated four or five patients in a ward, where they would be available to help nursing staff where appropriate, make themselves useful and generally familiarise themselves with the patients: taking histories, talking to the patients and where possible examining them.

I remember that I was allocated some patients on a ward where a neurosurgeon had beds. This particular consultant was a pioneer in neurosurgery. He was working in an extremely difficult surgical speciality and he was performing some breathtaking procedures. But many of his patients had tumours which carried a very high mortality risk. While I was on that ward and had been allocated some of his patients, three of them died during the week. I wrote to my parents and explained it badly! I said in my letter: 'I'm getting on fine and enjoying the work in the hospital. Three of my patients died last week. I'm going to a party tonight, It's Sam's birthday!'

They were apparently shocked, not understanding the circumstances. They wondered if I was fit to be let loose. All my fault for not explaining properly.

While all this was going on daily, we also had pathology lectures every afternoon. I must say I found it difficult to understand and learn my pathology that way. I found that I was able to get a grip on the subject by reading the text book that had been recommended: *Boyd's Pathology*. I found it readable, and interesting apart from the pathology content. Passing the pathology examination was a hurdle, not as bad as the anatomy examination, but still a lot of hard work.

'I've passed my pathology! Are you coming out to the Splot?' This was a pub only a step or two from 'Med Club' It was in a district called Splotlands. It was a small and unpretentious pub. A pint of bitter cost eleven pence (four and a half pence in decimal), and it was drawn straight out of the barrel. Great stuff!

We had courses of lectures in public health, hygiene and preventive medicine. Also medical jurisprudence or forensic medicine as we called it. That was a fascinating subject and we studied it using a book by Professor Keith Simpson, Home Office Pathologist, famous for his work in the acid bath murders committed by the murderer, Haig. We also had to pass an exam in small pox vaccination. That was a legal necessity because by law, every child in Great Britain had to be vaccinated against small pox. The only exception was if there was a medical contraindication or a valid conscientious objection. Then, in the late 1940s, the annual incidence of serious complications from the vaccination was greater than the annual number of cases of smallpox, so vaccination of children was no longer compulsory. We still vaccinated where requested or for travel reasons. Then, later in 1971 small pox was eradicated from the world altogether.

In the fifth year, students attended teaching sessions in clinics dealing with the other specialities in the field of medicine and surgery: ENT (ear, nose and throat) surgery, ophthalmology, dermatology, venereal diseases, and other branches of medicine. Venereal disease was very common at this post war time. Syphilis had been treated with the heavy metals, mercury had been used with very toxic effects, leading to the saying: 'One night in the arms of Venus leads to a lifetime on Mercury.'

We, as students were constantly aware of the presence of syphilis. It was said that it could mimic almost any disease, so it would be tactless to use the 'S' word when at the bedside. I nstead the clinical teacher might ask: 'Possible WR? (Wassermann reaction, a test for syphilis). Many other euphemisms were used around the bedside in the presence of a patient: neoplasm for   cancer, nicerea for gonorrhoea and others that patients gradually got wise to over the years. We attended VD clinics mostly in the evening and saw all the awful complications of venereal diseases. Syphilis was treated with an organic compound of arsenic called salvarsan. The treatment of gonorrhoea was sulphanilamide, one of the sulphonamide family.

Mr Jimmy Wade was one of the best surgeons in South Wales. He had retired before I entered clinical medicine as a student but stories of his prowess and his sayings lingered on for years. From what I understood he was radical, fast and efficient. That arose from the days when anaesthetics were not so good and surgeons had to work quickly. One of the things students talked about was his ability to pass a 'boogie', that is a solid flexible rod through the urethral tract into the bladder, (Ouch!). In some cases it was done to dilate a stricture that was preventing the patient from passing urine. The other symptom of a stricture was a slow heart beat. The urethral stricture was one of the more painful complications of gonorrhoea.

Every Christmas the more talented medical students put on a topical and comic show called *The Anencephalics* in which they sang comic songs that characterised their teachers. This was one of the songs, sung to the tune of Nellie Deane:

There's a stoppage in my flow Jimmy Wade,
And my pulse is getting slow Jimmy Wade,
It's entirely due I fear to a touch of nicerea,
Won't you please dilate my stricture Jimmy Wade?

During the fifth year, we had to attend one of the two maternity units for a month to learn how to conduct a normal delivery and all that went with it. During that time a student had to be resident on the unit. It was a choice between Glossop Terrace adjacent to the Infirmary or the City Lodge Hospital at the other end of the city. Four of us including my partner Paul, chose to go to the City Lodge. There was much more going on there and we all delivered many babies and were witness to some of the more complicated deliveries, high forceps delivery and Caesarean section.

We also were taught all about antenatal care and we took part in the clinics. I felt more than ever that I had become as competent as was possible for a student at that stage to feel, that is, competent in the management of a normal pregnancy and confinement. The disadvantage of the City Lodge was that it was a long way from medical school and at the same time we were supposed to attend lectures on public health and hygiene, lectures often at nine in the morning. They fed us very well while we were resident there, and there was a pub just opposite the hospital!

At some point in my fifth year I began to feel ill. I had a sore throat and a headache that wouldn't go away. I started staying in my room and I wouldn't take part in anything, work or pleasure. Some friends became worried, and after feeling the swollen glands in my neck they forced me to go over to the infirmary to see a senior medical registrar. I know now what they had in mind: had I developed a blood abnormality like leukaemia? I was entirely oblivious to this. I think I felt so ill that I just allowed myself to be carried along.

The registrar took the whole thing very seriously. He was very kind and explained that I must have a blood test. Still, for me the penny didn't drop but I think that my pals got a bit alarmed. Nothing was said about a possible diagnosis, not in my hearing anyway! I went back to my room and to bed and my friends brought me food and drink at intervals. In a few days the answer came: I was ordered to go home and not appear for work, or to attend clinics until I felt better. The Paul Bunnel test was positive: I had glandular fever.

I didn't feel relieved, I was not at that stage aware of the alternative diagnosis. I stayed at home for three weeks and even then it took me a while to get back to feeling normal. I missed quite a lot of work and it put me back a little bit.

In 1949 I started to take the final clinical examinations. Obstetrics and gynaecology came first. By the time I had reached this stage, now within striking distance of finishing the whole medical course, I started to get seriously down to work. The attack of glandular fever had put me back a little; it is well known that following this disease one becomes temporarily depressed, but I was now completely recovered. So I spent all day and every day following ward rounds, outpatients and clinical demonstrations in the company of a number of my friends.

When I wasn't in the hospital I spent more time than I ever had in my life immersed in reading. Having passed the obstetrics and gynaecology exam, the next hurdle was surgery. Finally when that was out of the way I took the big final exam, clinical medicine. I did actually find that exam the easiest of them all, partly because I had, admittedly rather late in life, discovered by now how to answer a question in an exam! The other thing that became clear to me was that it was a great advantage sitting clinical exams set by the teachers who had taught you, rather than by an unknown examiner.

So the final results came out and I was through! Next step, register with the General Medical Council, and after that, join the Medical Defence Union. When that was all done, my worries were all over! Weren't they?

I had no money, no job, I was entirely dependent on my parents, I had an overdraft that was very, very little compared with the burden that students have to bear today. It was really comical and amazing to see how irresponsible and rather wild medical students changed overnight, on hearing that they had qualified, to rather serious and dignified doctors. In fact it was slightly painful to see quite ordinary students become rather 'stuffy' and superior to their more junior friends who had yet to pass the final exams: offering advice in a patronising way!

The author and his fiancée (not yet officially so), Marjorie Ion in Cardiff on Marjorie's birthday. Celebrating the event with lunch at the Kardomah. Exam results still to come!

6

A VERY JUNIOR HOUSE DOCTOR

I was 23 years old and now a duly qualified medical practitioner, but without a job and an uncertain future! The first thing that Marjorie and I did was to celebrate modestly. We decided to get married as soon as possible. This rather put our parents in a state. We thought that we would apply for house appointments together, that is both of us in the same hospital. These jobs usually started on 1st April, so there was no time to lose! Father wanted to have an engagement party with an announcement in the press. There was no time for that so he settled for a brief notice stating that: 'The engagement is announced, and the marriage will take place etc, etc on March the 9th.' And that was that!

Marjorie's mother leapt into action and started making all the arrangements. Bobby, Marjorie's brother, at that time, a curate in Bromborough, married us in All Hallows Church, Greenhill Road, Liverpool. My brother Hilary was the best man and Joan Cianter, a student friend of Marjorie, was the bridesmaid.

We applied for several junior hospital jobs together but failed in every case to get into the same hospital. That is until we both applied for house jobs in Walton Hospital, Liverpool. We received a very nice and friendly letter appointing us both from the Medical Superintendent, Dr Mac William, affectionately known as Daddy Mac. Marjorie was appointed to be house physician on the tuberculosis block and I to a surgical ward.

After our honeymoon in southern Ireland, where there was no rationing and plenty of everything, we started work at Walton Hospital on 1st April 1950. We created a bit of a sensation. There were of course some of the more senior medical staff who were married, but they all lived out. Junior staff like us had to be on the hospital premises day and night. So we had to live in the   hospital – Daddy Mac arranged it magnificently!

We were given a large room in the part of the hospital usually reserved for more senior staff. It had easy access to the wards and we lived in comparative luxury. No wonder we received strange looks from the other housemen and women. This was a six month appointment for both of us, but Marjorie became pregnant half way through and she was threatening miscarriage. So she had to go home to rest. She was under the care of the obstetric consultant. Thankfully it all settled down in a month or two.

For me, that six months was the most strenuous and tiring time of my life. I was on duty and liable to be called at any time day or night, week in, week out! I have to explain that the emergency procedures that we would be asked to carry out were in no way comparable to what goes on in Accident and Emergency departments today. Walton Hospital was a very busy place and I was on the go practically all the time. I was off duty every Thursday from 2 p.m. until 8 a.m. the next day. Also every other weekend from Saturday midday until Monday morning. That worked out at about 130 hours work per week! It was the same for all of us as junior house doctors. It was very good experience and I learned a great deal that stood me in good stead later in life.

I was surprised how open the hospital departments were at night when all the office staff had left. For some reason that I can't remember, I needed to look at some old medical notes. I found that the records office was open; all I had to do was request the key from the porter's office. When we entered the records office we found all the records from the past were neatly and systematically stored. Marjorie wanted to look for the medical record of a great aunt, long dead. We had no trouble at all in finding it. Auntie Lizzie died in the early 1930s and all the notes of her last illness were there. The whole hospital was quiet, not a sound and it was as if the records were the ghost of all the dead patients; even from the days when the hospital had been a workhouse. It was eerie!

There were two surgical wards: T ward, in my care, that was for male patients; and S ward for female patients in the care of Dr John Harries. We shared our off duty but most times we were both on call. John's job finished in June and the hospital looked for a young doctor to replace him. I was left on my own for two weeks, no time off at all! Then a young southern Irishman came to replace John. Everyone took to him at once. He had a very nice way both with patients, colleagues and nurses. We thought ourselves so lucky!

Then after about two or three weeks he just disappeared. One day he was there, doing his job normally, and the next, with no word to anyone, he was gone. Nobody knew where or why then a rumour spread that he was something to do with the IRA! I was now on my own with no time off for some weeks. During that time, two events occurred that I found very upsetting.

The first happened in the middle of July. It was a Saturday afternoon, nothing much going on and I was sitting in the junior common room alone. A call came over the tannoy summoning me to T ward. The staff nurse on duty said: 'Doctor, a new patient has come in, sent by his family doctor. We've put him in the side ward, his notes are there with him. could you see him and write him up please. He's Mr John Kerry.'

'Right Staff, I'll see him now. Are any of his relatives still here?'

'His wife and his brother, they're waiting in the sitting room. Do you want me to stay with you while you're with him?'

'No thanks, I'll call you if I need anything, but could you make sure that his wife stays until after I've finished in case I need to ask her any questions.'

I went into the side ward, Mr Kerry was sitting up in bed with his hand pressed against his stomach and his fist clenched.

'Hello Mr Kerry, how are you feeling?'

'Oh' said he, 'I'd be OK if it wasn't for this pain, and it seems to be getting worse. My doctor says I've got an ulcer, and he says he's afraid it could burst! That's why he's sent me in today.'

'How long have you had this pain?' I asked.

'Quite a long time, several years probably, on and off, well ever since I was in the army. I was in Italy in 1944 when we chased the Germans out. I'm afraid we drank too much, you know! Vino, it was so cheap.'

'Where exactly is the pain, Is it where your hand is pointing now?'

'It's funny you should ask that because in fact it's moved and now it goes up to my shoulder and down my left arm, and it's much worse today.' He looked drawn and anxious.

I examined his abdomen, but there were no overt signs, no tenderness or rigidity, no evidence of a perforated stomach ulcer. His pulse was soft and poor volume and his blood pressure was abnormally low.

'Mr Kerry, I'm going to speak to your wife; she's here isn't she? And then I'm going to get another doctor to see you.'

'Well' said he, 'I hope he'll give me something for this pain, I'm beginning to feel awful.'

'I'm sure he will' I said.

I was fairly sure that Mr Kerry's pain was angina or worse, a cardiac ischaemic attack (coronary thrombosis). I went to the waiting room and spoke to his wife.

'Mrs Kerry, I am Dr Frost-Smith and I've just examined your husband. I am not happy with his condition and I am afraid the pain he is getting is coming from his heart. This is a surgical ward, as you know, so I'm calling for a medical colleague to see him and we'll...' A call from the staff nurse: 'Doctor can you come to Mr Kerry now please, he's having an attack.'

I had an idea that he was on the edge of an attack of coronary thrombosis, I went at once to the ward.

'Mr Kerry...' I started, then when I saw him I realised that he had just had a fatal cardiac arrest.

Oh my God! I felt for a pulse in his neck: nothing. I listened with my stethoscope over where his heart apex beat should have been: nothing.

Here was I, only just qualified and inexperienced, almost alone on a Saturday afternoon in the hospital, and faced with the task of having to tell the poor man's wife that although her husband had only just come in for some tests, he was now dead.

Staff nurse, he's gone... I mean he's dead! He's had a cardiac arrest.'

'You must go and speak to his wife, she's going to have a terrible shock. I'll come with you,' she said.

I returned to the waiting room. As I went in, Mrs Kerry and her brother-in-law jumped to their feet.

'What is it doctor, what's the matter, is Johnny all right?'

'I'm sorry Mrs Kerry, your husband has had a heart attack.'

'What d'you mean a heart attack? He's just come in to have his ulcer treated. Nobody's mentioned his heart!

'He has just, this moment had a fatal heart attack, I'm sorry. There's nothing we can do.'

'Oh my God, what has happened, where is he?' She rushed into the side ward before we could stop her, with her brother-in-law at her heels. They both rushed up to the bed and knelt by John's side, pulling at his hand.

'Johnny, Johnny wake up! Oh doctor, has he really gone? Oh Mary Mother of God help us!' She fell to her knees, sobbing and wailing uncontrollably, while we stood by helpless.

I really didn't know what to do next to help the poor woman. The modern young doctor has, I believe, helpful training in bereavement management, care of the patient under circumstances similar to this. I really felt helpless. I spoke to her brother-in-law quietly.

'We'll get you both some tea,' I said. 'See if you can get Mrs Kerry back to the waiting room nurse. I'll come there and explain to you both what happened.' I left them both for a moment to speak to the nurse, but came back to talk to Mrs Kerry when the nurse had brought them tea.

I explained as well as I could what had happened. She began to calm down and seemed to understand that her husband's pains, as well as being due to his ulcer, were due also to a heart problem getting more serious recently. This patient would have probably survived if there had been a defibrillator available to start his heart again. But they hadn't yet been developed for use in such circumstances.

That drama left me realising how inadequate I was, and how for a GP it would be essential to know how to manage that sort of emergency: that is the care, not only of the patient but of the relatives, in shock. Nobody could have stopped him from dying at that time. We had no training in cardiac massage or mouth to mouth resuscitation. That came years later.

I am sorry to say that I was going to have to deal with a similar situation, less dramatic, but more tragic, just a few weeks later.

Walton Hospital, for a young doctor like me, was a rewarding experience and preparation for life in General Practice. Admittedly there was always a senior colleague to call upon. But some emergencies happen rapidly and any young house doctor, who has completed all his training prior to qualification, but is completely inexperienced, could be on the spot and just has to get on with it. Sometimes there is no time to call for help.

It happened that it was again a Saturday afternoon. I was on duty by myself. If any surgical emergency was admitted it would be my job to write up the notes and if surgical action was needed, to call my immediate superior. This was almost always Mr Robert Borley. He was a senior registrar, on his way to becoming a consultant surgeon. On this particular Saturday, however, the call came to me on the tannoy to go to S ward, the female surgical ward. Not my usual responsibility, but it was my weekend on duty. I was there in a few minutes and the staff nurse on duty said: 'Doctor Frost-Smith, we have admitted a young woman to the side ward to one of Mr Tumarkin's beds.'

Mr Tumarkin was an ear, nose and throad surgeon and had two or three beds on both T ward and S ward. They were nothing to do with me. Mr Tumarkin looked after these patients himself. Nevertheless, any patient admitted had to be seen by the houseman on duty.

The nurse handed me the notes: the young woman, Mary Hindley, had been seen in the outpatients clinic and Mr Tumarkin had said that she was suffering from mastoiditis. He arranged for her to be admitted urgently for surgical treatment. The mastoid bone is part of the skull behind the ear. The lining of the air cells within it can become infected. This is usually a complication of untreated middle ear disease in which infected material from the middle ear leaks into the mastoid air cells. If untreated it can be very serious. It is possible for infected fluid to burst through from the mastoid into the skull and infect the brain, causing an abscess or meningitis. Today, such a patient would be treated immediately with antibiotics. The treatment then, had to be removal of a small piece of the mastoid bone to drain the infected fluid away.

Armed with this information I entered the side ward. The young woman's bed was shielded with screens and there was no-one with her. Her mother was waiting outside sitting on a chair by the ward door. I called for the nurse to accompany me to the bedside. I certainly did not expect to see what had happened. Mary Hindley was lying on her back with her eyes wide open and she was as pale as a sheet. She appeared not to be breathing. I felt for a pulse in her neck and listened for a heart beat. Nothing!

'My God,' I said 'she's dead, how on earth has that happened?'

'You'd better go and tell her mother,' said the nurse, 'she's outside the ward.'

'What the hell am I going to say to her, the girl is only nineteen?'

'I believe that the parents have been warned that the condition is very serious,' said nurse. 'So perhaps she will understand. I'll telephone Mr Tumarkin. He'll want to come in to speak to her mother, I'm sure. But you had better go now and tell her mother; She's going to be in shock. I'll make some tea and phone the consultant.'

This was the second time I had been faced with this situation. I have already said how ill equipped I felt to deal with sudden tragedies like this. It was just as well that I couldn't possibly know that this was just the first of many other similar events with which I would have to deal during my life. I would, however gain experience – hopefully. I went out of the ward to meet Mrs Hindley. She was sitting quite calmly reading the *Echo*.

'Er, Mrs Hindley,' I began. She put down the newspaper and looked alarmed.

'Mrs Hindey,' I began again, 'your daughter has been very ill I believe.'

'She's come to the hospital today as an emergency. Mr Tumarkin saw her this morning and said he would have to operate immediately: I think he said he would have to do a mastoidectomy. He did say that there was an immediate danger that the infection in her mastoid could spread to her brain. It's been so worrying.' She began to sob. 'Is she going to be all right? She had a terrible headache this dinner time before we left home.'

'Well' I said, 'I am afraid she is not all right...'

She interrupted with a start: 'What d'you mean, where is she, what has happened?'

'I am sorry Mrs Hindley, Mary has had a fatal attack of a brain infection. When I went in to see her just now, I am sorry to say she had already passed away. This mastoiditis that she was suffering from was, as I think Mr Tumarkin told you a dangerous disease. The infection spread to her brain quickly and I'm afraid there was nothing anyone could do to stop it happening. Mr Tumarkin is coming in to see her and he will explain to you.'

She covered her face with her hands and wailed. 'Oh dear God, Oh dear God. What am I to do? Where is she? Let me see her. How am I going to tell my husband and her sister?'

This was a terrible tragedy for the poor woman and my heart went out to her. I brought her some tea and later Mr Tumarkin came in to speak to her.

In my work as a house surgeon I spent a good deal of time in the operating theatre assisting Mr Robert Borley, my immediate boss. He was a senior registrar. He was seven or eight years older than I was and he was very clever. He had already taken and passed the FRCS (Fellow of the Royal College of Surgeons) qualification and would eventually be a consultant surgeon. We had one whole day in the operating theatre each week treating patients who had been on the waiting list for elective surgery, some of these were complicated and difficult. Robert Borley was very skilful and meticulous but very, very slow, painfully slow. I could hear occasional sighs from the anaesthetist. There were occasions when an operation which should have taken an hour and a half took Robert three hours! Nobody said anything, but one felt that it increased the risk to the patient. This was in fact born out by the results, I am sorry to say. In addition to these all day sessions we spent many hours in theatre dealing with emergencies which could come in any day and at any hour.

The chief of the team, Mr Orton was a big red faced man with an abrupt manner who certainly did not suffer fools gladly. When he was around, with his retinue of junior staff, I kept well behind. Robert Borley was noticeably anxious. Mr Orton did not come in on a regular basis but when he did come, a particularly difficult case was arranged for him to deal with. When he was operating I stood by and Robert assisted him. But I was always scrubbed up and gowned ready if I was needed. Incidentally no one at that time when I was there wore what today is call 'scrubs', that is freshly laundered trousers and tops and white boots. We all wore sterile gowns and gloves and a clean white cotton cap and of course a mask. It was a real pleasure to see Mr Orton operating on a difficult case. He worked very quickly and accurately. This was probably because he had worked in the 1930s when anaesthetics were not so efficient and speed was essential. Nevertheless he was a very skilled surgeon.

Later in the last six weeks of my job a new senior registrar came to replace Robert. Mr Patrick had served in the army as a surgeon right through the war and had developed a very skilful and rapid technique. It was a pleasure to assist him.

On one evening a young man came in with a straight forward appendicitis. Mr Patrick examined him and then said: 'Right Frosty this is a straight forward appendicectomy, you do it and I will assist you! I did operate and removed the patient's appendix. I was naturally apprehensive, but I had the feeling that with hard work and dedication I could be a surgeon, But I knew that I was not in any sense near to being adept enough. I also was certain that my future would be in General Practice. Throughout the operation Maurice Patrick kept saying: 'Come on Frosty, get a move on!' The patient recovered.

At the end of the six months period of the job I left and joined Marjorie at her parents' house, in Greenhill Road. Marjorie's parents were very hospitable and helpful to us. Marjorie was going to have to live there for some months until we were able to have a home of our own. Our first baby was due in February, but before that I was going to serve in the RAF for two years as a Medical Officer.

At that time there were usually only three ways in which a person could be admitted to the armed forces and proceed straight from being a civilian to being a commissioned officer without undergoing any officer training course. And that could happen if you were a lawyer, a priest or a doctor. There are, no doubt rare exceptions to this. So the day I joined the RAF I was commissioned with the rank of Flying Officer. I was summoned to Air Ministry at the beginning of November 1950 to be medically examined.

It was a very gentlemanly interview: nothing like the preliminary medical I had undergone in Scotland Road, Liverpool. I was ushered upstairs into a large office and welcomed courteously by a man whom I thought was probably a consultant physician. He asked me all about my past illnesses and talked a great deal about my health generally, and particularly about any medication I was taking, but he didn't examine me physically. I don't remember having any special tests. He told me to expect a summons to go to RAF Morton in the Marsh in Gloucestershire and there I would be inducted into RAF life and the medical routines carried out in the service.

7

RAF National Service

I travelled to Morton in Marsh a few days after my visit to Air Ministry. I was kitted out with battledress blouse and trousers. That I think was all. I don't know whether the large great coat was included, but I think it must have been, because I don't think I would have bought such a heavy garment. I was also given a forage cap but I was advised to purchase an RAF flat cap and a raincoat. I can't remember how my rank insignia showing my rank as a Flying Officer got on to my epaulets. I also must have been given the little brass emblems of a snake curled around a pole with wings above and topped by a crown to pin to my lapels signifying that I was a doctor.

There were about fifteen young doctors assembled at the RAF station for induction and we were under the care of a Warrant Officer. He was an experienced man who had spent his life in the service. He taught us all about the rules and customs, including the rules and niceties of the Officers Mess. He arranged various other lectures concerning the running of a Sick Quarters and managing a sick parade, and all the forms we would have to complete and the rules we would have to observe during our time in the service. We had a talk on rats, by Sergeant Rats Bowen! And a talk on kitchens by Sergeant Cookie Wilson. We mixed with all the other officers in the mess: pilots, engineers, padres. Not all were present for training, some were permanent personnel keeping the station going. It was altogether a pleasant relaxed month. When our time was up, we were to be posted to an RAF station as part of a team of medics, or as the sole medical officer. Some of us would be posted abroad, Great Britain was still an occupying force in Germany. Some would get home posting.

The RAF group Headquarters were responsible for postings. I had already been asked about my family circumstances so they knew that I was married with a wife soon to produce a child. The person to whom I spoke promised to try to get me a home posting.nI was posted as it turned out, to a small families camp in Cheshire. It could not have been better for me. Cranage is a small village near to Middlewich. The RAF station was devoted entirely to housing, running, and managing a families camp. That is several hundred families of ex-service men and their families who had been on active service during the war and were now repatriated to England.

The railway station was at Winsford just a short train ride to Liverpool where Marjorie was living with her parents. Immediately on arrival at the RAF station I made my way to the commanding officer's office – he was Squadron Leader Wilton. I knocked on his door and went in to his office, he welcomed me and said what sounded like: 'We've had a surprise cheque this morning.' I said 'Oh jolly good' ignorant, I was! I thought he had been awarded some money for the station. No, of course it was a surprise check, a visit from the auditors – not a welcome visit at all!

He directed me to the Sick Quarters where I was met by Flight Sergeant Hignet, a very pleasant man in his forties who was in charge of running the sick bay and who knew all the routines. He said: 'Good Morning Sir, let me show you around the quarters.'

It was beginning to dawn on me how strange it was that during my life up until now, and I was just twenty four, that my status had changed quite dramatically. I had actually done very little to bring this about. Just passed a few exams! In school I was Frost-Smith or Brian, (or Biv to my parents). Just a schoolboy and then quite suddenly when I entered university I became Mr Frost-Smith to all in authority. The day after I qualified I suddenly became Doctor Frost-Smith. It has been said that the wildest carefree medical student on qualification becomes a responsible and serious citizen, possibly even a little pompous! When I entered the RAF I suddenly was conscious of all these men saluting me and seasoned service veterans right up to Warrant Officer addressing me as Sir. That was because I was in uniform – but I just felt the same as I did when I was a schoolboy! I had a new name among my contemporaries: 'Doc'.

My duties were primarily as medical officer. Every morning there would be a sick parade. Any RAF personnel, men or women who

The Sick Quarters at RAF Cranage. A neat one story building with offices and two single cubicles that could be used for very ill patients. I am standing next to the Flight Sergeant with two male medical orderlies.

wanted to see the doctor would line up and come in turn into my office where I would see patients. The complaints were mostly simple: colds and coughs, minor injuries, cuts and bruises. Sometimes stomach disorders; but the service men and women on the base were nearly all young and healthy. In each case a form 624 had to be completed with details including diagnosis, treatment and disposal, the usual disposal was 'medicine and duty.'

In difficult cases I had access to RAF specialists who would advise me or see referrals. Family members could also call for advice or treatment, but mostly my contact with the families which was the main part of my job was visiting them at home on the RAF station in the married quarters.

Flight Sergeant Hignet was enormously helpful, having spent all his working life as a serviceman in the medical corps. I don't think I could have coped with the regulations without his help. I really don't know how he could have treated me with such respect considering that I was just a young whippersnapper with a recent medical degree, but service discipline prevailed and I respected him for his service, knowledge and loyalty.

In addition I had to tour the base, to inspect areas like the kitchens and all other places where health supervision was required. All this was just a small part of my work. There were several hundred families with children housed in wooden buildings, and furnished for each family. As I remember it there were large toilet blocks, men's and women's were separate. These families had been in a war zone, mostly Malta, and the living quarters here at RAF Cranage were comfortable but only temporary, until the families were settled back into civilian life. The whole station was under the care and jurisdiction of the commanding officer.

This was in fact a small General Practice and I was the GP. Before I had arrived, the medical care of the families had been done by the local GP, Dr Brown in Middlewich. I imagine that the powers that organised such camps, and there must have been others, had decided that the number of mixed civilian and service patients warranted a resident medical officer. The RAF would have had to pay Dr Brown when he attended RAF personnel but he could treat families as temporary residents in the NHS.

It was a complicated set up because my dispensary had a very limited selection of medicines and was geared to the treatment of normally healthy young men and women, for only minor ailments, whereas the medical requirements of the women and children I had to treat were entirely different. I called on Dr Brown at his surgery in Middlewich and found him to be very relaxed and helpful. He handed me a pad of EC10s, the NHS blank prescription forms on which I could obtain any medicines free from the local chemist in Middlewich, or if I wanted to prescribe for particular patients I could give them an EC10 that they could get dispensed at any chemist. There were no prescription charges in those days! Dr Brown also promised that he would stand in for me if I was away.

I managed to carry out my work satisfactorily with the help of the sick quarters staff. Apart from the Flight Sergeant there were four WAAFs – young women whose job it was to keep the place in order, clean and tidy and help with any patients. There was also a young service man who was the ambulance driver. I could use the ambulance which was a small van with two beds in the back. Apart from transporting patients, the ambulance was used for fetching supplies for the sick quarters. I used it on one or two occasions to take me to the station, but that was frowned on and I had to stop that!

A young AC2 (that is aircraftsman second class) came on sick parade. He entered the office, saluted and said: 'AC2 Travers sir.'

'Good morning Travers' I said, 'please sit down. What are you complaining of, what's the trouble?' He didn't appear to be very bright and was a little untidy.

'It's my ear, sir, It's paining something awful. I can't sleep because it's hurting so much when I lie down.'

'How long has it been like that?' I asked.

'It started last week, I'd been on a 'forty eight' (long weekend). Three or four days after I got back here, it was hurting all night, and in the morning there was blood and yellow stuff on my pillow. My ear was throbbing. I told the Corporal in the billet but he thought I was skiving. He told me to get on and pack my bed away. I said to him: "Look Corp' I'm telling you there's somethin' wrong, Look at my bloody pillow, it's all blood and mess. What am I going to do?"

'He told me to effing shut up and not to be a baby.'

'I'm sorry sir' said Travers to me, ' but that Corporal is a right bastard! But when he saw the mess it had made on my bed he changed his tune. He told me to go to the sick bay and see the Flight Sergeant. Flight sent me here to see you.'

'Let me have a look at your ear.' When I examined it with my auriscope, I could see that his tympanic membrane (ear drum) was perforated. There was some pus and blood in his auditory canal. He had a fever of 100.4° Fahrenheit.

'How did this happen, Travers?'

'Well sir, I was sitting in this pub, we was havin' a night out with friends, and I were sittin' next to this lass; she were a big girl, I think she were a police woman off duty.'

'I don't want to know about your social life, Travers.'

'The next thing I knew she had slammed me acrorst me 'ead! She had some punch, that girl. It were that what caused it!'

'How d'you know it were – was that.'

'It's been hurtin' ever since. I shouted "Hey what you think you're bloody doin? You've buggered me ear!"

'She hissed at me: "you just keep your effing hands to yourself."'

'We'll have to keep you here, Travers, for a few days and I will have to give you some injections for that infected middle ear.'

I tracked down Flight Hignet. 'Can we keep Travers in for two or three days? I'm going to give him some penicillin injections. Do we keep crystalline penicillin injection ampoules in our store?'

'I'm afraid not sir. We haven't got that up to date yet. I could order some from group stores at Hawarden, but it would take some days before it arrived, assuming that its on their list. I'm afraid nothing moves quickly when you order from the stores.'

'Thank God for Dr Brown' I said. 'Ask SAC Hopkins to take me to Middlewich and I'll get a supply from the chemist there.'

Middlewich was a very pleasant small town noted for the salt mines. I entered the chemist shop in the high street and was met by the pharmacist. I explained who I was and the connection with Dr Brown.

'If I write an EC10 for duracillin and 5ml of auristillae penicillin (ear drops), can you supply them?'

He smiled, 'Doctor,' he said, 'whatever you write on that prescription form, I must supply.' That is how it was then: uncomplicated!

Hopkins was waiting outside the shop and took me back to RAF Cranage. I had a supply of duracillin 200,000 unit ampoules, some sterile water ampoules and some penicillin ear drops.

Over the next three days we treated Travers with intramuscular penicillin three times a day and instilled the ear drops. The result was magical and he was able to return to his platoon. Flight Sergeant Hignet asked me to fill in a form detailing the disposal of the patient, but not the treatment. This would be sent to the adjutant. Stan, I can't remember his surname, but he was a native of Blackpool and his hero was Stanley Matthews the footballer! They were a pleasant pair, he and his wife. She was a supervisor in a telephone exchange.

Life on the camp was fairly easy going, I had to treat the civilian families, and now that I was able to use NHS prescription forms there was no problem. A woman came to the surgery and asked me to visit her daughter aged eight.

'What's the matter?' I asked.

'She has a very large, swollen and painful lump on her cheek, near her mouth. It started a few days ago and it's spreading quite quickly. Our house is number 48, can you see her today?'

'I'll see her this afternoon,' said I. 'I am going to inspect the kitchens this morning and I must see to that first.'

It was part of my duties to inspect kitchens and billets occasionally. When I entered the large kitchen and dining area that catered for 'the other ranks' I was assailed by an unpleasant smell and I have to say that the whole place looked messy. The sergeant in charge came up to me.

'Good morning sir, is this an official inspection, or just a friendly visit?' I did not like his manner.

'This is my routine inspection of your kitchen sergeant, and I must say I am not impressed. Look at those work tops there, they're all greasy and don't look clean. In fact I think the whole of the area looks pretty grotty. I advise you to get the whole area cleaned up. If the air officer commanding sees the kitchen like this, your feet won't touch the ground. You'd better see to it immediately; the air officer commanding is due to visit any time now.' He was full of excuses; but he had plenty of men to work for him, so I left him to it.

Meanwhile Marjorie was living with her parents in Liverpool and I was living in RAF Cranage. I tried hard to find a rented flat or house with easy access to the camp, but there was nothing, that is, nothing we could afford to buy. I went to the auction of a cottage in Little Budworth; I didn't even get a bid in. It was bought finally by someone who paid twice as much for it as I would have been able to consider! Our daughter was born in February at Liverpool Maternity hospital.

We were desperate to find ourselves a home, to rent or buy. Eventually a small end of terrace cottage was advertised for sale at £650. My salary as a flying officer was £700 a year. I would have to borrow all if possible, to buy this house because we hadn't been working long enough to save, so we had no money for a deposit. I went to see the woman owner in the village of Moulton. I tracked her down in her parents' house in the next street. She came with me to No 9 Whitlow Lane and she showed me around the house. It had two small bedrooms, a small living room, a bathroom and a built on kitchen at the back with plenty of room. The modern flush toilet was outside and there was a good garden shed.

'Mrs Asprey,' said I, 'I will arrange to bring my wife to see the house in the next day or two, but I am almost sure that we would like to purchase the property.' So it was arranged: Marjorie and her father came to see the house and approved. It was settled and Marjorie's father was kind enough to lend us all the money without charging us interest.

I bought Marjorie's brother's small motorbike; he now owned a car. I had to have transport to Cranage, and so it had to be the motorbike. I did arrive at the camp every day on time no thanks to that machine! It was undoubtedly the worst beast of a vehicle imaginable. Sometimes it would start with one kick, I mean the kick starter, but when that failed and I had run up and down the road with ignition on and in gear, I would gladly have kicked it into a pond. One evening at the camp when it was time for me to go home, the wretched bike would not start. Help is at hand I thought. I phoned the motor transport section and asked for help.

'Oh don't you worry sir' said the mechanic, 'I'll get it going for you immediately.' Brave words; an hour later he rang back saying: 'I've got it running sir and I'll bring it down to you, but I honestly think you'd better go straight home before it changes its mind, these two strokes are unpredictable!' The next morning, believe it or not, it started first time.

So now I was living out, in our own house in this village full of character. It was with great difficulty that I was able to have a phone installed, but when I explained why it was necessary, a line was fixed immediately. It was really great living at home and Marjorie loved it. Our daughter was three months old and it was lovely watching each development.

I was telephoned one morning by the station warrant officer. His job was a very important one, being responsible for all non-commissioned officers.

'Can I come and see you sir?' he said.

'Of course, Mr Dawkins. You can come now if you like.'

'I'll come straight away' said he.

Warrant Officer Dawkins, the equivalent rank in the army is Sergeant Major, was a mild mannered man in his 40s. Not a bit like the impression one gets of sergeant majors in the army.

'I'm sorry to trouble you sir,' he said. 'You see I'm not really ill, but I'm very distressed and I don't know quite what to do.'

'Sit yourself down Mr Dawkins,' said I, ' and take your time. Just tell me what is troubling you.'

He looked embarrassed and very ill at ease.

'It's my wife sir.'

Now I have to be careful: if Mrs Dawkins is living in married quarters on the camp, I can treat her, but if she is living some way away, she might have her own doctor. He answered my unasked question.

'We live in a married quarter on the station,' he told me, 'and I am upset by what is happening at home.'

'I think you had better explain, Mr Dawkins. Is this a sort of domestic dispute?'

'Well, yes and no, sir. Let me explain please: I am 42 years old and my wife is 38. We have been happily married for seventeen years. I have served in the RAF for twenty years. My wife, Judith is a school teacher and she teaches locally. We have always had a loving relationship and we have two children aged sixteen and fourteen.'

'That sounds like a very happy family, so why are you worried?'

'It's very embarrassing,' said he with a hand to his face. 'My wife is accusing me of being unfaithful!'

'Well, are you?' I asked, rather alarmed.

'I am certainly not! I have always been absolutely true to Judith, I have never deceived her. It's not in my nature to do so.'

'Then why, for goodness sake is she accusing you, has she seen you with someone and drawn the wrong conclusion?'

'No sir, but it is embarrassing for me to tell you. I have become impotent, I cannot perform, and Judith is convinced that it is because I am having an affair with someone. I don't know why it should happen to me and it is very distressing. I have explained this to my wife but she doesn't believe me. What do you think I should do? Is there any treatment when this happens to a man?'

'Do you feel well otherwise?' I asked. Are you depressed, or do you have any other worries about which you haven't told me?'

'No sir, nothing else is worrying me and I am perfectly well otherwise.'

'I should briefly examine you to make sure that there is no underlying cause. I need to test your urine for sugar, and take your blood pressure.

Will you bring me a urine sample?'

'I can do that now, sir if you give me a receptacle.'

I took his blood pressure and checked his urine for sugar. I also checked that his sexual organs were normal; no hydrocele (liquid swelling of the scrotum) and no evidence of testicular cancer. In fact I could find no physical abnormality.

'Mr Dawkins, I am no expert in these matters, but I do know that this can happen to some men. I do not know why and I have not ever read or heard anything that would explain it. Ill health or depression can be a factor that can contribute to it, but none of these things apply to you. I think you ought to try to explain this to Mrs Dawkins and tell her what I have said. I suggest that you take a course of some testosterone tablets; it could help. It has been used for this purpose, but I cannot guarantee that it will solve the problem, nevertheless I would like you to try it. As I said, I would also suggest that you tell your wife what I think and please say that if she would like to come and see me to discuss it I will be happy to talk with her.

'Please come back to see me in two weeks to make sure that there are no side effects from taking the tablets.'

Warrant Officer Dawkins seemed to be a little relieved, and so I gave him one of Dr Brown's prescriptions for methyl testosterone.

The RAF station was agog! The commanding officer was informed that the air office commanding, from group headquarters was going to pay us a visit and inspect the camp in a few days. It seemed that the commanding officer was slightly 'on pins'. We all had to make sure that our sections were smooth running and efficient. It did not really affect the Sick Quarters, we were always in a state of readiness for emergencies, thanks to Flight Sergeant Hignet.

Air Vice-Marshall Norton arrived in his chauffeur driven car and a retinue of high ranking officers that included my medical boss, Group Captain Coffee. After a brief consultation with the commanding officer, Squadron Leader Wilton, he proceeded to tour the station accompanied by us all. I do not remember what happened during most of his visit, but there were two incidents that I recall: We visited the kitchens, the place which I had felt was being badly run, untidy and messy. The air officer commanding took a good look around while we held our breath.

*A walk in the country near the village of Moulton
with Marjorie and baby.*

We could see what was coming and I had little sympathy for the sergeant in charge: I had warned him.

The air officer commanding walked up to the sergeant who was standing to attention at the head of his staff. 'The CO's office now,' he barked!

I was present when he reprimanded the sergeant. He told him that the state of his kitchens were a disgrace.

He said, and I remember it well: 'I will see to it that your cooking area is inspected very shortly with no warning and if you have not cleaned the place up you will face a court martial.'

I felt vindicated, and thought the air officer commanding was quite right to come down heavily on the sergeant who was slovenly in his management of the kitchens.

I did have a minor altercation with the air officer commanding. It was something to do with immunisations. He held his ground but he was non medical and didn't push his argument and although the series of re-marks faded out, I could see the commanding officer squirming and looking anxious. He felt that I should have kept quiet!

I was called in to the camp from home very early one morning. One of the civilian women Mrs Ada Veitch who was about 26 weeks pregnant had gone into labour. She had been booked to have her baby at Stepping Hill Hospital near Stockport. The midwife had been called but hadn't yet arrived. It took me about 30 minutes to get to the camp and I made my way straight to the house or hut that was her home.

'When did your labour start?' I asked, 'and where is the baby?'

'It was stillborn' she said. 'Why did this have to happen to me: I have been perfectly well and living quietly, haven't I Tom?' She said to her husband.

Her husband answered: 'She started having pains in her tummy this morning and we thought it was just bad colic; she's not due for another three months. But then she started bleeding and we knew the pregnancy was going wrong.'

'Have you been attending antenatal clinics at Stepping Hill hospital?'

'Oh yes, I have been several times, the last was two weeks ago and they said the baby was OK, they could hear the baby's heart.'

'Where is the stillbirth now, where have you put it?'

There was a knock on the door and the midwife came in.

'Hello' she said, 'what's going on? I'm nurse Craydon.'

'I had the baby an hour ago, it was stillborn.'

'Oh dear, I am so sorry, according to my notes you were about 25 or 26 weeks pregnant, is that right?'

'Yes, I think so, according to the clinic.'

'Now' said Nurse Craydon, 'you just lie down flat and let me examine your tummy. The uterus has contracted down and there appears to be no bleeding. So it looks as if all is well. Now, where is the stillborn?'

'We didn't know what to do with it did we Tom? It was very small and shrivelled, I think it must have been dead for some time. I couldn't bear looking at it.' She held her hand to her face silently sobbing. 'It came with the afterbirth an' all.'

'Now don't you worry sweetheart,' said Tom. I didn't know what to do and Ada was so upset. In the end we just put it in the coke stove.'

'Oh my God' said I.

'Don't tell me you did that,' Nurse exclaimed. 'You're not supposed to do that. I am supposed to complete a stillbirth form to send to the local health office and to the registrar of births. What am I going to do now?'

'Listen,' I said, 'this foetus was only 24 or 25 weeks old, wasn't it. So according to the law it couldn't survive even if it hadn't been stillborn. We must treat this as a miscarriage, so don't complete the form nurse. I will telephone the registrar tomorrow and explain.'

They all looked relieved. 'Now Ada, I just want to check you over to make sure that you are OK.'

I performed the usual check ups and all seemed to be in order.

'I'll call in and see you tomorrow morning. You can get up and sit in a chair, and just have a little walk across the room.'

With that I left them and went home to bed, a little worried by what I was going to tell the registrar in the morning.

I telephoned the registrar after sick parade in the morning. 'Hello, I'm Doctor Frost-Smith. I'm the medical officer on Cranage RAF station.'

'Good morning doctor, how can I help you.'

'We had a birth last night, Mrs Ada Veitch. I am pretty sure that the foetus was only about 25 weeks.'

'That is all right, said he, has the midwife called? She will complete the usual stillbirth form.'

'I don't think it was a stillbirth, it was an abortion at about 25 weeks.'

'She still needs to send in the form, she will know what to do,'

'I am afraid that is not possible, you see the husband disposed of the dead foetus before we arrived.'

'Oh my God,' said he. 'I don't want to know. Don't tell me any more. This hasn't happened. Please just forget you told me. Are you satisfied that it was under 28 weeks, making it a miscarriage?'

'Yes, I am quite sure.'

'Well don't tell me any more, I don't want it recorded. You'd better tell the husband that what he did was irregular and probably illegal. Make sure that they understand, and don't take it any further. All right, we'll just leave it like that. Goodbye.'

I was relieved that the matter was settled, and that afternoon I visited the family again and found that Ada was quite all right after her experience.

I continued in my duties until three weeks later, I was due for two weeks leave. I arranged it with Dr Brown who was so helpful. We went to see Marjorie's parents and stayed with them for the whole of my leave.

The day I returned to duty at Cranage, Stan, the adjutant phoned me.

'You've been posted,' he said, 'to RAF Lytham St Annes near Blackpool. You must report there on May 24th.'

That would give us a month to move out. I wasn't pleased but there was nothing that I could do about it.

8

THE GOOD, THE BAD AND THE UGLY

We managed to sell our little house in Moulton, and made a nice profit of about £200. I paid back my father in law and that was that. I still had the blessed motor bike!

Marjorie and our baby went to her parents in Liverpool. We were so lucky to have that option. I made my way to Lytham as ordered to join the medical staff at the camp sick quarters. I would have to live on the station on my own, National Service men were not allocated married quarters. I was hoping that we could find a flat to rent. I was due to be de-mobbed at the end of November, so it would be a short term lease.

At the end of my first year of service I was promoted to Flight Lieutenant. That was automatic and not due to any merit, but I was very surprised when I arrived at the medical centre to find that the National Service medical officer in charge had the rank of squadron leader. This was, I understand very unusual. He had no higher medical qualification that would entitle him to jump from flight lieutenant to the senior rank of squadron leader. He was not a pleasant man and considering that we were about the same age and seniority in other respects, he was unfriendly and rather high handed.

My posting to Lytham from Cranage was quite an upheaval. I couldn't understand the reason for it – with just six months to go before my de-mob it did not make sense. My reception at the sick quarters did not help. Fortunately this guy, the doctor, left soon after I arrived, but I still think of him as being the 'Ugly' component of my move to Lytham! The 'Bad' and the 'Good' would follow!

There was another doctor at the medical centre. He was a civilian, not in uniform and he never seemed to have any duties. He spent the whole day working on his vintage Alvis at the motor transport section. He would appear at lunch time all oily and greasy to have his lunch in the mess – I just do not know how he got away with what he was doing.

I believe that he had probably been taken on as an added temporary doctor to help deal with an influx of men into the RAF station. Both of these two strange doctors left the service about a month later. He was the 'Bad' component, and I do not see how his employment in the RAF at Kirkham could be justified. He was a dour Highlander, no friendly small talk.

I was very busy examining hundreds of new arrivals of the rank aircraftsman. It was a very perfunctory examination too. I also had to do routine medicals for pilots, and I had never done this before. But I read up the detail of what was required and with the help of the friendly flight sergeant I managed. In addition there was the day to day work of the sick parade and dealing with accidents and emergencies.

I buttonholed the flight sergeant and asked him some questions: 'How was it Flight, that my predecessor carried the rank of Squadron Leader; not usual for National Service doctors?'

He was a man you could talk to. He was like Flight Hignet at Cranage, friendly, helpful and smiled.

'You see sir' he said, 'the doctor found out that the establishment here was for a squadron leader medical officer. This was because in a way, doing the pilots medicals was a specialised job. This was also a very important high ranking station with a group captain as commanding officer. He pointed this out to the commanding officer and very quickly his promotion as acting squadron leader was gazetted.'

The very next day I called at the commanding officer's office. I had not met him before and I liked his friendly and relaxed manner. He had been a Battle of Britain pilot, and something of a hero! He understood immediately.

'You are quite right doctor, I will see what I can do. Within the next few weeks my promotion was gazetted and I sewed on the extra thin stripes on my epaulets. That put me on an equal footing with all the pilots on whom I had to do the routine medicals. But there was something far more important that happened! My pay went up from £750 per annum to £1,200 per annum. This was a huge raise for me and I immediately started looking for furnished flats. That was the 'Good' element.

A furnished flat was advertised in the local paper: No. 5 Lake Road, Lytham-St Annes. I went there at once and found the owner. The house was very near where the sea would be when the tide came in far enough. The flat was on the first floor and I thought it excellent: well appointed, well furnished, a large sitting room and two bedrooms. The ground floor flat was occupied by an army major and his wife, a very friendly couple. The flat was advertised at £4-10s per week, but the owner told me that because I wanted the tenancy for only six months, the rent would be £5. I agreed and fixed a date to move in with Marjorie and Helen.

The house next door: No. 1 Lake Road, was the home of George Formby – I don't know if he was ever there and I never heard a ukulele playing!

Marjorie was delighted and her father drove her and Helen up within a few days to move in. The fact that my salary had increased was crucial. I could not have afforded the rent on my previous salary. That and the profit we had made on the sale of 9 Whitlow Lane enabled us to buy an old 1937 Morris Ten. Now we could drive off to Liverpool when I was off duty. So the move to Lytham was, after all a very good one.

I really enjoyed the remaining time at Lytham. I made a few friends one of whom one wanted to buy my motorbike. I did warn him very clearly of its nasty habits and I insisted on his trying it out for a few days before making up his mind. He bought it in spite of all I had said; and he still remained my friend; moreover he agreed to pay me £60 for it, that was the sum I had paid for it!

The other man I became friendly with was the Anglican padre. He was Welsh from near Wrexham. We talked a lot about life in the RAF. He was a single unmarried man and he was able to lead a very full life on the camp.

Earlier on, soon after my arrival, there was a dining in night. These were formal affairs and all the men wore their dress uniforms. It was understood that National Service men would not own one and we had been told early on at our induction that it was permissible to attend in battle dress. At that point however I was a new arrival and I was told I was to be Mr Vice! The dinner in the officer's mess was formal. The commanding officer sat with his guests at the centre of the transverse table at the top, forming a T shape. I, as Mr Vice was right at the bottom end of the stem of the T. Drinks were served during the meal and each diner paid for it himself; it would appear on his mess bill. Although my tongue was hanging out I could not afford such luxuries. I did notice that in particular, my friend the padre drank freely. He told me afterwards that all of his salary apart from his living expenses were donated to the church, so, as he said he might as well enjoy life.

At the end of the meal, the port was circulated strictly according to custom. The port is circulated to the left, You must pass it on to your neighbour on your left, using your right hand and he takes it with his right hand. When all the glasses were filled, The commanding officer stood and called out 'Mr Vice, The Queen.' Whereupon I, as Mr Vice, stood up and called in a loud voice 'Gentlemen, The Queen'. That little ceremony over, and I, like all assembled drank the toast, but I can't remember whether it came free or not, but I believe they still adhere to this ritual.

I spent six months at RAF Lytham. The station was full of jolly RAF pilots in training. There were parties in the mess several times while I was stationed there but once I had moved out to our flat I did not go to many functions. Near to the end of November it was time for me to leave the service. I was ready to carry on with my intention of entering General Practice. I now had three years experience and was beginning to gain confidence. I do not think that I committed any *faux pas* in my service years, but I did wonder, and still do, why I was moved.

During the last few days, an RAF recruitment officer called to see me. I cannot remember whether he was civilian or uniformed. He asked me if I would like to stay on with a permanent commission. If I did follow that career I would get a permanent rank of squadron leader with a little more pay, and rise eventually to wing commander. This was not what I wanted in life, so I politely declined the offer and explained why. It occurred to me then, that if I had behaved incorrectly at some point and I certainly was not aware of anything, surely the RAF would not be offering me a permanent commission.

That interview was the end of my National Service and I shed my uniform and returned to the civilian life of a young doctor looking for a job.

9

HOSPITAL LABOUR

In late November 1952 I was de-mobbed from the RAF, out of uniform and back into civilian life with a wife and a daughter, I must try to find work. My ambition was the same as always, but at some point I must complete six months in an obstetric house job which is most desirable for entry into general practice. Looking back at this time then, in 1952, there was a queue of young doctors whose aim was the same as mine. It was going to be difficult in the short term; I would have to apply for every post in the north of England with reasonable access to Liverpool. The job in obstetrics would require me to be resident in the hospital and when I would be off duty I would want to be able to visit Marjorie. This would be possible now we had the old Morris Ten. In the meantime I had to find some hospital or GP work to earn some money.

At that time there were several agencies advertising for young doctors as locums in General Practice or hospital. The Medical Insurance Agency was the best one, but there was also a local agency in Liverpool. I made my details and requirements known to both of these and was duly put on their list. The first job that turned up was as houseman on U ward at Walton Hospital. I was accepted for this and found myself working for Dr Kemp, the consultant. He was especially interested in gastric and duodenal ulcers and most of the ward consisted of patients who, under his recommendation were having a continuous milk drip orally! He insisted that this was the best way to calm an acute ulcer.

The sister on the ward was an efficient Indian girl who was very domineering. I would go into U ward having the intention of taking blood from a patient who had been admitted with a haematemesis, (vomiting blood). The patient was to have a blood transfusion and when I had obtained a sample of his blood, grouped and cross matched, I would set up the drip. But immediately I appeared she would say to me: in a very bossy way: 'Go to Mr Alexander, doctor, and take some blood for group-ing' or some such thing. Ward sisters could be very bossy!

'That is just what I am about to do, sister.' I would then try to get my own back by saying: 'Have you got the tray ready?' But she was always one ahead: 'The tray is there by his bed, the third bed on the left side.' She would know perfectly well that I was aware of his bed position, but she had to win!

My immediate senior was an older woman, Dr Mary Foley. I got on well with her and I was very sad when I learned that while she was on holiday with a friend her car was hit by an articulated wagon jack knif-ing. They were both killed; very sad.

During this time at the hospital I did not have the luxury of the big room that Marjorie and I had enjoyed when we were both working on the wards. I had a room down in the annex at the bottom of the drive. There were several young housemen there who were good company. I did of course go to Marjorie's parents' house at 11 Greenhill Road when I was off duty. The job was undemanding and I found Dr Kemp an easy boss and a friendly man. I spent three months at Walton Hospital. At the end of this period I was asked to stand in for a GP as his locum for a week at his single handed practice just off Lodge Lane, near Smith-down Road Hospital. He was going to be away for two weeks, but needed to cover a gap of the first week of his holiday before another doctor arrived for the second week of his absence.

On the first day there, after I had finished the surgery the receptionist asked me: 'Will you call and see Mr Kelly at number 29 Sundown Place, just opposite the hospital. They say it's urgent, he has a pain in his chest.'

I went immediately, and found the house. I had to knock and wait until the door opened and a harassed looking middle aged woman came to let me in.

'You're too late doctor,' she said. 'I think my husband is dead!'

I followed her upstairs and found the patient lying on his bed and ob-viously he was dead.

'When did this happen?' I asked.

'Just now' she said. 'I heard a noise like he was banging the floor with his stick. He always did that if he wanted anything. I just thought he wanted another cup of tea, so I didn't hurry, it was a few minutes later

I went up and, Oh God, there he was, dead; I couldn't believe my eyes. 'I couldn't have done anything to revive him, even if I had run up the stairs.'

'No' I said, 'he has had a sudden cardiac arrest. Nobody could have saved him. How long has he been ill?' I asked.

'Well he hasn't really been ill. He was working yesterday at the docks. When he came home last evening he looked tired and said he would go straight to bed after his tea. But he didn't finish his meal, he said he had indigestion. He was all right until now. Oh my God what am I going to do?'

'How old is he?'

'He's just fifty seven. He had a birthday party last Saturday and he was complaining of indigestion even then. He drank very little: not his usual way.'

'Has he seen Dr Holmes, his doctor recently?'

'No, the last time he was at the surgery was last May, more than six months ago, and that was because of a cut on his right hand that he did at work.'

Oh hell, I thought. What am I going to do? I cannot sign a death certificate if he hasn't seen a doctor within the last two weeks. Dr Holmes will be away for the next fortnight, and he has not attended the patient recently.

'I am very sorry that this has happened. He has obviously been suffering from a bad heart ever since he was complaining of indigestion. Have you got any children who will come to be with you now?'

'Oh yes, we have three boys and a girl. Jack the eldest lives just around the corner. He should be at home now. He's on holiday.'

'I will go and break the news to him and ask him to come to you now,' said I.

After seeing Jack I went back to the surgery and spoke to the receptionist. 'How long is Dr Holmes away for?' I asked.

'He's going to be away for two weeks,' she answered.

'Mr Kelly died before I arrived at the house. I cannot sign the death certificate. I have never seen him before. I must phone Dr Holmes in case he has attended the patient, and Mrs Kelly has forgotten or perhaps did not know. It's a possibility. Have you the doctor's phone number?'

I asked.

'Yes, he's in Bournemouth,' she said and gave me the phone number of the hotel. I phoned the doctor and explained what had happened.

'You will have to inform the coroner,' he said. 'I haven't seen Mr Kelly for ages.'

Just as I thought. I knew that it was the right thing to do and did so. I went back and explained to the family. They, of course were distressed at the sudden loss of husband and father. I explained the law to them and I think they understood the position.

The next locum job came to me again from the agency in Liverpool. A Dr Solomon and his partner Dr Sharpe wanted a temporary assistant for a few days. The surgery was at 13 Walton Hall Avenue. Dr Sharpe was going to be away for a few days and they wanted temporary help. It was just after Christmas, a busy time for doctors. There are two main reasons for this: at Christmas time, the only holiday that a factory worker could expect to get was two days; Christmas Day and Boxing Day.

The day after Boxing Day, many people, understandably, did not feel like going back to work after the Christmas celebrations. The only way that they could avoid losing pay was to visit the doctor and ask him for a certificate. In addition, this time of year was a peak time for the spread of infections: colds, influenza like infections and stomach disorders. Also, it was the time when bronchitis and other pulmonary infections were commonly made worse by the dust laden fogs and smoky atmosphere. These were problems common in Liverpool then. There was always a queue of patients waiting for certificates in the surgeries.

I called on Dr Solomon and presented myself. He asked me for a reference – I did not expect this and was rather surprised. I felt that my past employment history and medical qualification should have been enough. He smiled.

'You would think so,' he said. 'In fact the last locum I took on disappeared at the surgery time. He was supposed to come in early and start seeing patients before I arrived. I couldn't think where he could be. Then I found him upstairs in the little rest room. He was fast asleep and I had a job waking him. It turned out that he was addicted to barbiturates. It was an impossible situation; he had committed some blunder at his last locum job and had narrowly escaped being crossed off the General Medical Council Register. He couldn't remain here of course. I told him that he should seek advice to get himself clean of the addiction.'

'Well,' I said, slightly shocked, 'I can assure you that I have no hidden vices, but I will bring you my last reference this evening when I come in to help with the surgery; and you won't find me asleep.'

'That's fine' he said, 'I hope you're not offended.'

'Not at all, I quite understand.'

Looking back on it: I think Dr Monty Solomon was a very good GP and a wise man. He helped me a lot. He and his partner had a fairly big practice and looked after their patients. Two drugs that emerged at that time that improved patients' quality of life were Butazolidin for arthritic pain, it was dynamic in its effect. And Franol for patients with asthma was very effective. Neither drug, like many more that emerged around that time is used very much now.

Most patients who attended the surgery while I was there would tend not to consult me. They quite naturally preferred to see their own GP; as most still do today. So nearly all my work for that practice consisted of home visits.

The practice premises were very basic. As far as I remember there was no extra money allowed to employ a receptionist or secretarial help. General Practitioners were, then, and still are independent contractors and nearly all used their own premises to work from and many of them lived on the spot. Some bigger practices might have employed ancillary help, but many or possibly most practices were single handed, sometimes employing an assistant. It was later that it became advantageous to form partnerships.

The last locum in general practice that I did came to me again via the Liverpool Agency. A locum GP was needed to temporarily take over Dr Downan's practice in Shaw Street, not far from Lime Street Station. I replied and said I would take the job. The very next day I climbed the steps up to this old terraced house in the busy street and knocked on the door. A tired looking older woman came to the door.

'Are you the locum?' she asked. I replied that I was and asked her to show me the consulting room. She grimaced and opened the door of a small room on the other side of the entrance hall.

'The patients wait in here,' she said. 'Morning surgery starts at nine thirty, and evening surgery at six.'

Then she showed me into the next room. It was pretty bare: there was an examination couch and a large roll top desk on which were lots of papers, hospital letters, NHS certificates, prescription pads and nothing else. There was a small wooden filing cabinet holding patient's record cards.

'Is Dr Downan here?' I asked, thinking perhaps that he was ill.

'No, I'm afraid he's not, you're on you own. Will you be able to manage for the week until my husband comes back?'

'Oh yes, and I think I'll be all right.'

'Good,' she said and with that she left me and went upstairs. The first patient soon arrived – a middle aged woman with a small child clinging to her.

'How can I help you? What are you complaining of?' I asked.

'It's not me, it's Ronan here, my son. He's been coughing all night poor lad and doctor usually gives me a bottle of 'Lictus.'

'Right,' I said, 'let me see his chest.'

'Can't you just give me the bottle of 'Lictus' like doctor does?'

'I'll look at his record card. What's his surname?

'Hughes,' she replied, 'that's his father's name, not mine.' I turned up the card, but it was absolutely blank.

'I must examine his chest, just pull up your shirt Ronan, there's a good lad.'

I rummaged in the desk, opening all the drawers. I could not find a stethoscope. Just a letter, a pawnbroker's receipt: 'One Stethoscope: Ten shillings and sixpence!' I hastily shut the drawer and found my own stethoscope. Nothing but a few dry sounds. I took his temperature and it was normal.

'I'll give him what I think Dr Downan gives him.' I gave him some Linctus Scillae Opiatus pro inf, (a children's cough linctus).

'I think that will help him.'

'Where's the doctor?' she asked.

'I'm afraid I don't know, he's away for a week.'

'I'm sure he's helping some poor soul,' she said. 'He's got a poor old mother over in Dublin, perhaps she's ill. He is such a kind man you know. When I was in trouble,' she nodded at Ronan, 'he was so kind and helpful.'

She went out and the next patient came in. A burly rough looking man. 'What can I do for you?'

'I just want me note, it's due today.'

'What is wrong with you?' I asked.

'He just puts Debility.'

'Yes, but what is the matter with you?'

'I dunno, he's the doctor; he knows. I got the sack from Lucas in Aintree and had a nervous breakdown. He puts three months on the sustificate.'

'I'll make it out for a month. I'm not allowed to put more because I'm not your proper doctor,' said I with my fingers firmly crossed.

'Oh well, I suppose it'll have to do. When's Downan back anyways?'

'Hopefully, in a week.' He left without another word.

I visited some of Dr Downan's patients, his practice extended some miles out of Liverpool, up Prescot Road, Old Swan and even extending right up Muirhead Avenue. The striking thing was that his patients stuck to him; they all made a point of saying how kind he was, he always called when asked and never grumbled!

It was one of his patients who spilled the beans. He was caught driving under the influence of alcohol, and the police threatened to take his licence away; it had happened before. It went to court with a judge adjudicating. He apparently was let off with a fine providing he had himself admitted to the infirmary to be 'dried out' that is why he needed you to cover for him. Somebody must have spoken up for him.

It was while I was doing this locum that one night I was called to an address in the centre of Liverpool, not far from Shaw Street. A Mr Murphy with a very marked 'Scouse' accent telephoned: 'Is that you Doc?'

'I am afraid that Dr Downan is away, I am standing in for him. What can I do for you; what seems to be the trouble?'

'Can yer coom to me wife, Aggie, she's banged her 'ead and she's that dizzy, I dunnow what to do.'

'Where do you live, and what name is it?'

'Murphy, and the address is 49 Stable Street, it just off of Byron Street.'

I had a good map of the city centre, and I soon found the house. It was in a terrace of what used to be called 'back to backs'. Most of these houses were condemned, but a few remained. I knocked on the door and was asked to enter by a tall rather scruffy looking man.

'In 'ere,' said he. An equally untidy looking woman was sitting on the only chair in the room, holding her hand to her head.

'What has happened to you?' I asked.

She pulled her hand away revealing a rather doubtful looking rag, possibly a cleaning cloth. She had a laceration about an inch long, bleeding. It had to be sutured, but first it had to be cleaned!

'Is it possible to have some hot water please?' I asked.

I put a curved cutting needle in a saucepan together with a needle holder, forceps and scissors. Mr Murphy produce a kettle of boiling water and I poured some over the instruments. Having washed the cut and threaded the needle with silkworm gut I put in two stitches amid groans from the patient. I powdered it with Cicatrin powder and covered it with a dressing and plaster.

'Now then' said I, 'tell me what happened? Where is the furniture, are you moving house or what's going on?'

'We had a row' said Mr Murphy, 'and we chopped the lot up.'

'Why on earth would you do that?' I asked. He shrugged and remained silent.

'I'll tell you why, doctor' said she. 'He said that he was feelin' cold, and why wasn't there a fire. I got annoyed. Do you know what it's like living in this hell hole of a slum? I told him, "I've been out at work all day cleaning at the 'ospital, while you've been sitting on your arse doing sweet FA." "I can't help being out of work," he said.

'So he picked up a chair and threw it at the wall, it came to bits and he tried to light a fire with it. "Alright," I said, if that's the way you want it." And I took the chopper and started hacking at the other chair. Then it got out of hand. That's what happened.'

I left them, there was nothing more I could do and I certainly wasn't going to take sides in a family row.

'Come and see me at the surgery in a few day' I said. And with that I left them to sort out the mess. In due course she came to the surgery and I examined the cut; It was clean and healing.

'So how did it happen?' I asked again.

'Does it matter,' she said. 'It was an accident, that's all. Thanks for your help. We'll get sorted. I've been to the 'Assistance.' (The National Assistance Board 1948, created by Clement Attlee's government to replace the Poor Law).

'They've found us some chairs and a table, they've also found 'Arry a job on the council, temporary like, but it'll see us through.'

Soon after this, in March I replied to a Medical Insurance Agency advertisement offering an obstetrics house job at Boundary Park Hospital, Oldham. The consultant, Mr Percy Foot required a house officer in 'Obs and Gynae', commencing April the first. I applied immediately and went for interview that week. After a few questions, he accepted me, to start on the first day of April. I was delighted. The hospital was fairly new and I met the Registrar who was to be my immediate boss. Dr John Howes was Irish, from County Cork and he had all the charm and friendliness we usually attribute to the Irish! At this hospital I learned all the obstetric and gynaecology skills I would need when I entered general practice. My whole life, day and night was spent in learning how to manage a normal delivery and most importantly how to organise good antenatal care.

On my second day at the hospital, a patient was admitted around lunch time. Her doctor had sent her in because it was her first baby, and she was far on in labour. He, Dr Howes found that the baby was presenting as a breech, that is bottom first. There was no previous pregnancy by which to judge that the baby's head would pass through the pelvic aperture. Taking X rays to make these judgments during antenatal care is not acceptable. Ultra sound imaging could have helped, but in 1950 it was not available. So often a first baby breech presentation would be an indication for delivering the baby by Caesarean section. For this patient, admitted in advanced labour, there were no options: she was about to deliver! She was admitted to the labour ward, John scrubbed up, and I was available to assist if required. We all held our breath! To speak plainly: if, after the breech of the baby had been delivered, it was clear that the head would not pass through the pelvic aperture, there could be no live birth.

This situation demonstrated clearly how important antenatal care is. This breech presentation would have been noticed during the last weeks of the pregnancy at an antenatal care clinic, and if the baby could not be turned into a head, or vertex presentation then Caesarean section would have to be considered. It was not clear why this had not happened. It is possible that the mother did not notify a midwife or doctor until labour had commenced; it does happen.

So now, John was in a situation where the head must be delivered, and there is a limited time because the umbilical cord is now being compressed between the emerging head and the pelvis   outlet. The midwives and I present in the labour ward stood by, tense with the anxiety of the drama. The baby's head is soft at this stage and providing that difference in its size and the size of the outlet is not too great, then hopefully it will squeeze through. When the legs and both arms were delivered. The baby's body was hanging vertically, held back by the head in the pelvic outlet.

It is interesting to note here that the first difficulty in this delivery was the bringing down of the baby's arms. John had managed this, but not everyone is so fortunate. The last German Emperor, Kaiser Wilhelm II, born in 1859 was a breech delivery. The doctor involved was English: Wilhelm's mother, Princess Victoria (Vicky), the eldest daughter of Queen Victoria was English and would have no German doctors. The delivery was difficult, to say the least. In bringing down the baby's left arm extra force was used that severely damaged the plexus of nerves in the left armpit.

It was clear, as soon as Wilhelm was developing, that his left arm was shorter and thinner than his right arm and was almost useless. He could not even cut a cake with his left hand. He was subjected to a variety of horrendous devices to try to force him to use and develop the arm, all to no avail. He was made to ride on horseback because in that position the defect was less obvious although he repeatedly fell off and was replaced immediately. His mother rejected him because she felt that as the Emperor he had to appear to be perfect in mind and body. Historians claim that this rejection caused him to hate the English and to be bombastic and impetuous making tactless pronouncements on sensitive topics without consulting his ministers. He dismissed The Chancellor Bismarck and launched Germany into a bellicose new course in foreign affairs that led in a matter of days to the First World War.

Bringing down the arms can be difficult sometimes but when that is accomplished the baby's weight provides gentle traction on the head with a little moulding. With a finger in the baby's mouth and lifting the body slightly John eased the head out and in a few seconds we had a live birth and a healthy crying baby. We were all delighted and I was impressed at John's cool efficient handling of the birth.

The experience I gained at Boundary Park Hospital gave me the confidence and the expertise to handle many confinements in my years as a GP. Especially to make sure that every maternity patient had proper antenatal care, and to recognise possible complications before they happened.

I followed Mr Percy Foot on his ward rounds, assisting him in the operating theatre and learning from him all the time. He was a brilliant surgeon. He also pioneered ground breaking work on artificial insemination, which gave happiness to many women who, up until then had failed to conceive.

Mrs Caroline Buckstead was the young wife of Handley Buckstead, a successful and wealthy business man from Oldham. They had been married for several years and now she was pregnant for the first time. They consulted Mr Foot privately. She attended our antenatal clinics regularly but she was always seen by Mr Foot himself. In August she was admitted to the labour ward and Mr Foot personally attended. At about ten o'clock that evening she was delivered of a seven pound baby boy. It was a normal birth.

I was on duty at the time but I was not required to attend the labour. There was some talk at the time, I think. Should NHS hospital doctors attend private patients? I am not sure but I think on that evening I was the only obstetric house doctor present. Percy Foot met me before going home and asked me to call him if I was worried. About half an hour later the labour ward called me. I had not gone to bed and I went down immediately. Mrs Buckstead was still in the labour ward and the sister was worried.

'We've delivered the placenta' she said. 'but she's still bleeding. The baby is fine. I'm putting a lot of pressure on the uterus and she's had Ergometrine (from ergot and used to make the uterus contract) but the uterus is still flaccid.'

'I think you'd better repeat the Ergometrine, sister. I'll telephone Mr Foot and ask him to be ready to come. Her blood group is O Rh positive isn't it. I'll take some blood and go down to the lab and cross match a pint and we'll give it straight away.'

I spoke to the boss and told him the situation. He said he would come later.

The laboratory was always available all night, the key was in the porter's office. There were no pathology technicians present and it would take too long to bring one in, so I cross matched a pint of O Rh positive blood. I had done this many time before and it takes only a few minutes. Although the group of the blood that I was about to give was the same as the patient's group, you have to mix the two bloods on a slide to make sure that there is no agglutination or clumping of the cells which would indicate that the two bloods were not compatible.

All was well and I hurried back to the ward and set up the drip transfusion forcing the drip rate to obtain a rapid transfusion. Ten minutes later, and the blood transfusion was almost finished but Mrs Buckstead was still losing heavily. Sister was really anxious.

'You'd better 'phone Mr Foot again; this is really serious.'

More blood needed. I dashed back to the lab and cross matched another pint. I set it up and phoned again, this time with a degree of urgency in my voice. 'Right, I'm coming,' he said. But it was a full twenty minutes before he arrived. By that time I had cross matched a third pint of blood and was setting it up when the boss appeared. He took a quick look at the patient. He felt the uterus bimanually and said: 'Get the operating theatre ready and call the duty anaesthetist urgently!'

Scrubbed up and in theatre he opened the abdomen with a lower segment transverse incision and tied off both uterine arteries. It was no good. Poor Mrs Buckstead never came round from the anaesthetic. She had lost too much blood and she died in surgical shock. I felt terrible; I had pumped in at least three pints of blood into her as fast as I could, I felt I could not have done more. How long did it take Mr Foot to come I asked myself? But of course I said nothing to anybody. God knows how the boss felt. Make no mistake, he was a first class obstetric and gynaecology surgeon. But he misjudged the situation.

I met him in the office about half an hour later. He was, understandably not his usual breezy self. He had talked to Mr Buckstead who was obviously terribly upset, though apparently his grief was a little moderated when he had held the baby boy in his arms. Mr Foot thanked me for my efforts in rapidly transfusing the patient and said little more to me. I was told that he had been cross with the nurses; why? I cannot think. It seemed to me that the staff had behaved perfectly, perhaps in the upset of the situation he spoke hastily.

At the time, 1950, the British maternal mortality rate was about ten per hundred thousand births. Now, in the year 2016 it is about one per hundred thousand births. One third of the deaths in 1950 were due to post partum haemorrhage and most of the others were due to puerperal infection. During pregnancy the female immune system is not so active and that renders the patient more likely to succumb to infection.

During my job at Boundary Park Hospital Marjorie stayed frequently with her brother, Bobby who at that time was vicar of Tintwistle about ten miles from the hospital at Boundary Park. When my six months as house surgeon was over we returned to stay with Marjorie's family in Liverpool and I started looking again for short term jobs to tide me over until I should find an assistantship in general practice, hopefully in the north of England.

10

COUNTRY PRACTICE

In October 1953 I was a little sad at finishing my job at Boundary Park Hospital. Obstetrics is a happy sort of speciality – dealing with mothers and babies. I did just toy with the idea of preparing to study for the Diploma of the Royal Society of Obstetrics and Gynaecology, but my aim was always to become established in general practice.

Quite a few young GPs have added this diploma to their qualifications, but the criterion of whether a principal GP takes you on as a possible partner seems to depend more on whether he or she likes you and thinks that you will fit in to the practice, and be liked by the patients. The income in general practice at this time depended almost entirely on the number of patients registered in the practice. My boss in my first assistantship said to me: 'Most patients like to be treated by a kind, and listening doctor, not a clever one with multiple qualifications.'

As well as searching for a suitable practice, I had to think about a better car than the old Morris Ten. It seemed to be reliable enough; it had taken us on several quite long journeys without breaking down, but it was sagging! The chassis had rusted away to such an extent that it had a noticeable dip in the middle and the doors were not fitting properly. It would definitely not do.

I called at the West Coast Motor Company in Liverpool. I had my eye on a Morris Minor. They said immediately that there was a waiting list of at least a year. I explained to them that I was about to enter general practice. They suggested that I write to the Ministry of Trade and that they would probably give me a dispensation that would allow me to purchase the car immediately. They would also allow a longer period to pay back a loan on a hire   purchase agreement. The cost of the car was about £450 and I could afford the necessary one third deposit.

Now that that problem was solved, I continued to examine all the advertisements that arrived from the Medical Insurance Agency and the local Liverpool office. There were many jobs on offer at this time. Assistants were needed in Barnsley, Bolton and Bromborough; that was the one mentioned earlier where the boss spent his time wining and dining with his pals, leaving the poor assistant to do all the work. There were many other doubtful offers, but none seemed especially suitable. The government through the NHS provided a financial incentive for a GP to employ an assistant, but it was obvious that in all cases there was no offer of an eventual partnership in the practice. That offer I did not expect.

One GP in Harrogate made it quite clear that he had been told by the NHS Executive Council that he had too many patients; the maximum allowed at that time was 3,000. If you had more than that, you did not get paid the capitation fee for the excess number. He was an extremely pleasant man who told me that if I worked for him, he would be seeing all the first time visits of patients but I would be welcome to follow up the cases. The practice in Bakewell sounded ideal, but there was a snag: the accommodation provided for the assistant was a flat and access to it was by a steep flight of stairs. It was quite unsuitable for us with an infant and a pram.

At last and quite soon I was notified that a Dr Jack McFeeters wanted an assistant in his practice in Tattershall, Lincolnshire. He was quite clear: it was for a period of about eighteen months only and at the end of that time his son would be joining him. It was a country dispensing practice and I liked the sound of it. A small house was provided rent free for the assistant in the neighbouring village of Coningsby. I applied immediately and was asked to come for interview: Marjorie and I were both asked to attend. We drove there one bright Sunday morning through Buxton and Chesterfield, through parts not known to us: Newark and the little town of Sleaford; it was quite small then! Eventually we arrived in the town square in Tattershall at lunch time. We stopped outside a pub in the square opposite the large church that looked like a cathedral. The castle built by Ralph de Tattershall and rebuilt by Charles Cromwell treasurer of England, was also visible from where we sat while having our lunch. We were captivated!

After a quick lunch we made our way through the square and found Bramhall, the home and surgery premises of Jack and Molly McFeeters.

We knocked and Mrs McFeeters opened the door and welcomed us. We chatted and eventually I was asked about my life, my education, and the posts I had held since qualifying. We talked about our families: the McFeeters had two children, a young man, about to join his father in the practice and a daughter soon to be married to a fellow student, both Cambridge graduates in English. All seemed to be satisfactory. The McFeeters wanted to be sure that when they went on holiday, we would move to their house to keep everything in order. Jack McFeeters made it quite clear that he proposed to share all work with his assistant, including night calls. I was very impressed with his fair-minded attitude. He showed me the surgery and dispensary, they were very small compared with the equivalent in towns; but I expected that, and compared with Rhydronnen in Tregaron they were palatial!

We were taken to see the small house in which we would live while I worked in the practice. Then at a quiet moment when Mrs Mcfeeters was talking to Marjorie, he took me to one side and quietly said: 'I am sorry to ask you this, but I am afraid I must. Are you a Protestant, or are you a Roman Catholic?' I replied immediately 'We are Anglican, Church of England.' He gave a sigh of relief. 'I thought so, but I had to ask!' Knowing that both he and his wife were born and bred in Northern Ireland, it all made sense and it did not worry us in the slightest.

He told me then that he would be delighted to welcome me and Marjorie and we were to live in the small house, number two Church View, opposite the church in the adjacent village of Coningsby. We were to start at the beginning of November and for the first week I would live in their house to give us time to move our belongings into our new home. We were excited at the prospect, it was just what we wanted.

I had to learn how to dispense medicines for patients. All the drugs that we would use to treat the patients were in the dispensary; some in large Winchester bottles on a table and some in smaller bottles on several shelves upon which there were also bottles of tablets. There was a large collection of ointments and creams in large jars, many of whose names were unknown to me.

As I understood it at that time, a GP like Dr McFeeters would be paid a capitation fee for each of the patients on his list. I believe, the capitation fee was nine shillings (45p) per patient and for that fee he would be expected to supply all the medicines used to treat his patients. When this contract was agreed, the cost of almost all the medicines used was very small, but very soon, in the 1950s essential expensive drugs started to appear. GPs complained that they could not supply these drugs out of the capitation fee of nine shillings. It was therefore agreed that if one of these 'specials' was to be used the doctor could write a prescription, submit it to the pricing authority and be reimbursed.

This made a huge difference and of course it only applied to dispensing doctors. Non-dispensing GPs would write an NHS prescription for everything. It took me a week to get used to the names of the medicines. One day, early on I wanted a simple cough medicine for a patient and I was told that a large Winchester labelled 'Bronch' was very good for a productive cough. 'Just put about half an inch in an eight ounce bottle and fill up with water' Dr McFeeters said.

'What is in it?' I asked.

'I'm not sure,' he said, 'Molly makes it up; it's a good expectorant mixture,' and indeed it was!

It was suggested that we should take our half day off on Thursday each week. Jack and Molly McFeeters liked to have Wednesday and they always went to Lincoln. They took with them boxes of garden produce from their own garden and I think they sold it to a local café where they lunched each week. They returned loaded with large bottles of concentrated medicines as well as creams, ointments and tablets for use in the practice. All these were placed conveniently on the shelves and in the dispensary.

The number of patients attending a morning or evening surgery was small, perhaps five or six, unless there was an influenza epidemic or something similar, but even then, most consultations would be by home visit. There was only one consulting room with an examination couch and a desk. When we were both, at the same time, seeing patients, I used the dispensary for a consultation. If I wanted to examine my patient lying down, we would temporarily swap and I would use the other room that had the examination couch. It may sound cumbersome and difficult, but I did not find it so. We were constantly swapping over either to access the couch or to dispenses for a patient. In effect Dr McFeeters would be available at all times when we were seeing patients in the surgery, for me it was really like being a trainee.

Morning surgery finished at ten am, then the boss would consult the visiting book. This was a diary produced by Burroughs Wellcome, free, for the use of GPs. When opened there was a month to view and several double pages for each month. Listed down the left side were the names of patients and along the top the days of the week. It was like a spreadsheet and each square, opposite the patient's name and below the day and date would be placed a forward slash indicating that a visit was required. At the end of the day we completed each mark making it a cross for visit done and marking the next visit for that patient in the same way. Dr McFeeters was very keen that the diary was accurately completed so that it was a dependable record.

On average, between us we would make about 30 to 40 visits a day. In today's climate that sounds like a huge number of 'house calls'. The practice covered a wide area in Lincolnshire and most patients had no means of attending the surgery. Except for acute new calls, most visits were repeats and often consisted merely of asking how the patient was feeling and generally progressing, possibly checking blood pressure or re-dressing an injury. Collecting an empty bottle to be refilled when we returned to the surgery. The repeat prescriptions were placed on a shelf in the waiting room and magically disappeared later; collected and delivered back to the patient. No doubt a neighbour or someone was able to carry out this service.

When morning surgery was over we retired to the kitchen and over a cup of Ovaltine prepared by Molly McFeeters, we discussed the patients who had attended morning surgery, and I was allocated visits to be done that day. It was all quite relaxed. Dr McFeeters had worked as a GP in the 1930s before the NHS started and had bought his first practice in Cambridgeshire. He told me that he had made a mistake buying a very small practice. Although the larger practices were more expensive, the income generated was greater and if the greater workload could be managed it was a better proposition. So he had moved to Coningsby and Tattershall.

When a big investment had been made in buying a practice, it was very important to keep in touch with your patients. That might mean regular visiting, especially in a country area before the NHS. It was like buying a business and sometimes a bill was not paid for professional services. Indeed in many cases the patient would be unable to pay and if appropriate would try to compensate with gifts of farm produce.

We got on very well, the boss and I. He was very fair in every way and very gentle in any criticism. He was outstanding in the skills of general practice; I could tell that his patients loved him. I found out, that before he settled in the present practice he had worked on his own in Cambridgeshire. he had discovered that there were more cases of a type of Muscular Dystrophy among the children there than should have been, statistically. Because it was 'fen' country it was fairly circumscribed and intermarriage was more common. He wrote up and analysed all the relevant cases from which he produced new information about the inheritance of the disease. He submitted this as a research paper and was awarded, not only the M.D. degree but also a gold medal for outstanding work.

It so happened that the first week I was there, and living in the McFeeters' home it was time for the annual flower show. This was a big occasion in the area and the committee had asked Miss Gwen Berryman to open the show. Gwen Berryman was a regular actor and contributor in *The Archers*. She played the part of Doris Archer in the series which started in the early 1950s and is still going strong. Marjorie and I had listened to the programme from the beginning, consequently I was more than interested to meet one of the principal actors. Doris was a very interesting character and was able to tell me a lot about the characters in the programme.

At this time, the writer of the programme had written in the death of Grace Archer, Philip Archer's wife in the play and had caused a national outburst. There are still rumblings going on today – *The Archers* is still broadcast on Radio Four.

In July, while we were living in Coningsby our second daughter was born in the hospital at Boston. The consultant and all the staff were very kind and helpful. Marjorie had been admitted early because of a degree of pre-eclamptic toxaemia. But soon after Rachel was born, Marjorie improved and both were able to return home. Our house was warm and comfortable but the winter that year was severe. Heavy snow fell and I found it difficult to get around on my visits to patients. It could have been much worse in a hilly area of the country. But the Lincolnshire Fens were as flat as a pancake! Bunker's Hill was the only hill in the practice area the gradient of which was so gradual it was hardly noticeable.

One Saturday morning when I was on duty on my own, a Mrs Houghton phoned and asked, 'Is that Dr McFeeters?'

'I'm sorry, he's off duty this weekend, I am Dr Frost-Smith, his assistant: can I help you?'

'Oh doctor, I'm so sorry to call you. I am Mrs Houghton and it's my son Timmy, he is six years old and he is not at all well. I think he has a temperature and he's shivering. He says his throat is sore, but he won't let me look at it. I think I can see a slight rash on his stomach. I'm so worried in case it's the scarlet fever. Can you come to see him?'

'Yes, of course I'll come, where do you live?'

'We live on Tebbit's farm. My husband rents the farm from Mr Hogarth.'

'Where is that exactly?' I asked.

'Do you know the road to Kirkby on Bain? Well, the lane to our farm is on the right hand side about two hundred yards after you pass the road to Tumby. I am afraid there's a gate to open, we can't leave it open because there are sheep in the field. The house is about 200 yards up the lane. It's an unmade road so go carefully!'

'Right, I should be with you in less than an hour.'

I put my coat on and picked up my case. When I looked out of the window, I was horrified to see that it was snowing heavily, those large wet flakes of snow covering the ground several inches deep. Oh my God, I thought; I hope I can travel through this lot. I told Marjorie where I was planning to go.

'You be careful,' she said 'and take it easy through this lot. It's going to be skiddy.'

I took the road to Kirkby on Bain and followed Mrs Houghton's directions. The main road was not too bad, there had been traffic along it that morning. I found the gate on the right and opened it. Fortunately I was wearing wellingtons, the snow was about four inches deep. I could see a few patches of grass where the snow was thinner. Oh Hell, I thought, it looks as if I am going to be stuck here; bogged down, I shouldn't wonder. I edged the car though the gate and closed it after me. There were lots of trees heavily laden with snow. I could not see any lane.

Now this is where the dead flat countryside is an advantage. My car was a little Morris Minor. No four wheel drive or winter tyres, but I proceeded 'crabwise' across the slippery soft snowy ground the 200 yards to the farm house. Mrs Houghton greeted me gushingly, obviously pleased to see that I had managed to get to the house.

'Thank you so much for coming,' she said. 'I have been so worried; but now you must have a hot drink first, to warm you up on this cold day. Just sit down and I'll bring it to you.'

As if by magic she produced a steaming cup of coffee. I could smell a delicious fragrance, and when I tasted it I realised she had added some rum to it; that set me up!'

'Now, tell me about Timmy. How long has he been ill?'

'Oh, just two days. He was out with his father trying to help him bring some sheep in to home fields. We can keep an eye on them there and it makes it easier to take them food and make sure there are no sick ones. He came back to the house for dinner and shouted for me.'

'Mum, I don't feel well and I've got a terrible sore throat.'

'He wouldn't let me look at it but he was shivering and felt hot. I took him straight to bed with a hot water bottle. Then I noticed the rash.'

'Is he in bed now?'

'I'll take you up to him.'

Timmy was a fine looking lad of about six, as his mother had said. But he was flushed and restless.

'Now Timmy, here's the doctor come to see you. It's Dr Frost-Smith.'

'Mum, can I have a drink, my throat is so sore?'

'I'll get some water for you now, I won't be a minute.'

'Hello Timmy', said I, 'I would like to have a look in your mouth. Can you open wide please?'

Timmy was a co-operative lad and kept his tongue down and that gave me a good look at his tonsils. They were both swollen with a coating of yellow pus. 'Thanks Tim, that's fine. Now let me put this thermometer under your tongue: good, just close your mouth gently; don't bite it.' I looked at it after half a minute. He had a fever of 103° Fahrenheit. His mother came back into the bedroom.

'Let's have a look at Tim's chest,' I said. There it was: a typical scarlet fever rash: red on pink skin.

'Well, there's not much doubt about that. I'm sure Timmy has scarlet fever. We'll go down stairs and I will explain to you.'

'Oh dear me, what are we going to do, what are you going to say? I was afraid of this. It's dangerous isn't it? My nephew had the scarlet and he was terribly ill. They thought at one stage that he wouldn't survive. What am I going to do? Poor little Tim!'

'When was it that your nephew had the condition?' I asked.

'Oh it was ten years ago. He's a big strong lad now. But little Tim has always been rather frail when it comes to catching things. He had measles last year and was quite ill with a bad ear infection. It's so worrying, and my husband is away in Boston all day.'

'Now listen to me, there is no need for you to worry. Scarlet fever can be cured these days. It's not dangerous any more. We treat it with Penicillin. It's caused by a germ called Streptococcus Pyogenes which is sensitive to Penicillin. No doubt you will have heard of that new antibiotic?'

'Yes I think I have heard that the Americans discovered it.'

'Well, actually Alexander Fleming first discovered it in London. But it was developed by Florey and Chain in Oxford who persuaded the Americans to take it; the firm that took on the project produced a useable drug in time to save very many lives in World War Two.'

'I will prepare a bottle of children's Penicillin for Tim to take. Can you get your husband to pick it up from the surgery later on? Give Tim one teaspoonful four times a day. It's got a nice taste so I think he'll like it.' I left Mrs Houghton feeling a lot happier and I managed to steer the car back to the main road successfully.

Part of my duties was to hold a branch surgery at Mareham le Fen. This is a small, rather pretty village about two miles from Coningsby. We held the branch surgery there twice a week I used to go once a week alternately with Dr McFeeters. One of the houses on the left hand side had a small extra room built on the side of the house. It was like a small greenhouse. There were two chairs and a table filled with Winchester bottles of concentrated mixtures, the same as the ones back in the surgery. There were also some empty medicine bottles and a large jug of water to dilute the concentrated mixtures.

The house was occupied by Mrs Hale who put out these items in time each day there was to be a surgery. She also showed me into the adjoining room in the house where there was a couch that I could use to examine a patient if it was required. It was usual for only three or four patients to attend, and these would normally be residents in the village. If there were any home visits to make, and there almost always were three or four, the messages were left with Mrs Hale to pass on to me. She always gave me a cup of coffee and sat with me to have a chat. I enjoyed doing that relaxed surgery.

Some of the calls I made were to very old cottages constructed by wattle and daub. On a framework for the house the walls were constructed by making panels of thin branches woven into upright stakes held between the main framework. This is the wattle, it is then daubed with mud, clay and animal dung mixed with horse hair. This method of construction has been used for 6,000 years and is very similar to lath and plaster used sometimes today for interior walls. Two or three of the houses I visited were made in this way; the odd thing that I noticed, was that the floor in some of the upstairs rooms were sloping slightly and seemed to sway as I walked on them. I was a little surprised; it felt as if the whole structure was swaying and likely to collapse at any moment. The first time I ventured in to one of these swaying bedrooms to see a patient who was in bed, I must have looked alarmed, but I was assured that I was quite safe.

There are many assets for one living in the flat fen country, apart from the ease of driving in the snow. The sky from sunrise to sunset is visible, and the whole of the horizon is also visible so that the landscape with its variation of colours and other beautiful features can be seen. The rivers, wide, deep and flowing slowly are a prominent feature. It is a very restful scene.

When the McFeeters went away on holiday, Marjorie and I moved into their house. It was a large house standing on its own with a tennis court and a large vegetable garden. They had a full time gardener, and much was made of vegetable production. Molly McFeeters told me that the profits from selling vegetables paid for the gardener. When we were living there for the two weeks that Jack and Molly were away, we had a few duties aside from running the practice. We had to feed Snowy the cat and feed and walk Chang the Pekinese.

We had to keep the house in order and feed the Aga cooker with solid fuel. This was a little hazardous: the hod full of fuel was too heavy for Marjorie to lift high enough to pour the anthracite into the stove. I think that possibly this task was done by the gardener normally. So that was one of my jobs and you first had to dislodge Snowy from her spot just over the opening. The whole exercise turned out to be quite a full time job for the two of us, and with running the practice as well there was no spare time.

One day, when I returned home, having finished the home calls, I was just looking forward to some lunch but Marjorie called me as soon as I entered the house.

'There's been an emergency call. You'll have to go at once to this woman. She phoned ten minutes ago. she's pregnant and she's gone into labour a week early. Her husband is away all day at Horncastle and she cannot contact him. She had to walk to the telephone box in the village. She has tried to phone the midwife but she is visiting Lincoln Infirmary. They're trying to get a message to her but it will be an hour at least before she will be able to attend. You must go at once, never mind lunch.'

'Where does she live?'

'It's Mrs Hilda Watkins and she lives at number three, Sunset Cottages, North Kyme Fen.'

I picked up all that I needed from the surgery and hurried off. I knew where North Kyme Fen was – I had visited a Mr Greatorex there. It was half an hour before I arrived at the cottage. I found Hilda Watkins on her own and lying on her bed.

'Oh Doctor, I am so worried, I think the baby is coming, it's a week early you know. Nurse Jackson said she was coming this afternoon to do the usual checks, but I have failed to contact her. I'm so glad you have come. Can you cope with this alone?'

'This is your second baby isn't it? I've looked at your record. You had your first nearly three years ago in Boston Maternity Unit, a girl and she weighed just six pounds. Is that right? Did everything go well then?

'Oh yes it was a normal birth.'

'And where is she today?'

'She's with my sister, at her home in Mareham- le-Fen.'

'Well, let's have look at you. Just lie flat on the bed. How often have the pains been coming?'

'Oh every five minutes or so. There's one coming now— Ooh,' she tensed, and the abdomen hardened.

I examined her. The foetal heart was going strong at 120 per minute. Her blood pressure was normal, her colour good. Internally: the cervix was fully dilated and the head was coming down.

'Do you have a hot water system?' I asked.

'Oh yes, we have a Rayburn, the water should be good and hot, and the stove is on full.'

I retrieved my sterilizing box with the instrument that I might need, but hoped I wouldn't need. The stainless steel box complete with a spirit burner, had been given to me by Marjorie to cope with emergencies like this. It was long enough to hold the Wrigley's forceps and everything else, that might be required. The Wrigleys forceps also, hopefully would not be needed.

I scrubbed up my hands and arms and re-assessed the situation. Everything was progressing and the baby's head was coming down nicely in the birth canal. She was pushing bravely with each pain and I encouraging her, 'Push Hilda, come on you're doing well!'

Just when the head was about on the perineum, it stopped. I listened to the foetal heart: it was going fine, still about at the same rate. When the next pain came, I called 'Push, Hilda,' but there was no movement of the head. It seemed to be just stuck at the pelvic outlet. Right, I thought, I'll have to use the Wrigley's Forceps. They were already sterilised.

I had never used my Wrigley's forceps before in a home delivery, but I had used them in hospital. They are 'outlet forceps' used when the baby's head is visible at the opening of the birth canal. They pose no risk to mother or baby. The use of other types of forceps have an increased risk the higher the head is in the birth canal. I have seen a high forceps delivery when I was a student at Cardiff City Lodge Hospital. The procedure struck me as being rather forceful, to say the least. These days high forceps are never or very seldom used. If an accurate estimation showing disproportion has been done, an elective Caesarean Section is preferable.

The application of the forceps blades is straightforward. The left blade is inserted first in a downward and forward motion in the mother's left side. Then the right blade similarly. The blades lock and end up in a horizontal position. So, having scrubbed my hands well with soap and water, I poured a few drops of chloroform on to a pad of gauze, and held it over Hilda's mouth.

'Just breathe this in, Hilda' I said. She took a few deep breaths and immediately relaxed. I took the gauze pad off her face and switched my focus to the baby. The well lubricated forceps slid in easily around the baby's head, inserting the left blade first, holding it pointing upwards, then as it slid in it assumed a horizontal position. This I knew was the correct way to insert these forceps. Now the right blade was inserted in the same way. They locked. It only needed a minimum of traction first in a downward direction and then more horizontally and upward.

The baby's head was delivered easily, then the shoulders with the arms and then the legs. I held him up by the legs and cleared his mouth with my finger. There he was, a boy who gave a hearty yell. At that moment there was a bang on the door. Nurse Jackson appeared looking flustered and out of breath.

'Oh my goodness,' she said, 'I came as soon as I got the message. Oh, that's wonderful you've got a lovely baby boy.'

Nurse Jackson took over from me, cutting the umbilical cord, wrapping the baby up and handing him to Hilda who gave a sigh of delight.

'What is your name doctor?' she asked.

'Frost-Smith' I replied.

'No, no, your first name I mean.'

'Well,' I said a little embarrassed, 'it's Brian actually.'

'Well then, that's what his name is going to be.'

'Well, I am flattered,' I said though I was a little confused.

The same thing happened on another occasion, I cannot   remember who was the patient when it occurred. Obstetric forceps were invented by the Chamberlen family. They were French Huguenots and escaped to Britain fleeing from religious persecution and settled in London. Pierre was the first in the family to carry the title Doctor. The other members of the family were all surgeons. It is thought that he invented the forceps. He became obstetrician to Henrietta, wife of Charles I.

Today, It would not be acceptable to do what I did that day in North Kyme Fen. One could say that a desperate situation requires desperate measures, I had no choice. If I had phoned the nearest hospital at Boston, ten or twelve miles away and an ambulance had been sent, complications could arise. In Liverpool, when I worked in Huyton, there was a Flying Squad Service, mainly for treating a retained placenta or a post partum haemorrhage. There was nothing like that available in 1950, not in Lincolnshire. In later years I did carry out home deliveries, sometimes in an emergency situation, but they were all normal births with proper antenatal care.

We lived, happily in Coningsby, loving the environment, the people and the work for about eighteen months. Then the time came for us to leave as young Dr McFeeters was coming to join his father in the practice. I was very sorry to leave and I still dream occasionally about the remote pub at Old Bolingbroke with the beer barrel containing 'live' beer on the counter. The huge churches in Coningsby and Tattershall and the vicar who called out to me as he cycled by: 'I'm coming to see you tonight for another bob's worth!' The shilling prescription charge had just been introduced!

11
Huyton GP

We were very sorry to leave Coningsby, but we knew all along that our time there would be about eighteen months. Dr McFeeters and I agreed on a probable date for our leaving. I started straight away looking for my next job. We asked the Medical Insurance Agency to send us details of advertisements for assistants wanted in the North West region. We looked at several and we did not find one that appealed. Then my eye caught an advertisement for an assistant with possible view to a partnership in Huyton. This situation would be ideal for Marjorie, because it was close to her parents' home, so I applied to Dr Charles Garson immediately. I noticed the name Garson at once because I had known a doctor of that name when I worked at Walton Hospital. Marjorie and I were asked to attend for interview at 81 Bluebell Lane. It all went well and the Garsons told us that there was a house in Seel Road in which we could live. It would be rent free. So all was agreed, nothing was said about a possible partnership, that would come later if I was found to be acceptable.

Once again, Marjorie, with our two daughters aged four and one respectively, moved in with Marjorie's parents at eleven Greenhill Road. I returned to Coningsby to prepare for the removal. I bid farewell to the McFeeters and asked the doctor: 'I think you may agree that we have got along together very well indeed for the time we have spent here and we are very grateful to you both for your kindness and your help to us.'

'Yes' Dr. McFeeter said. 'I have been very satisfied with how things worked out and we are sorry you are going, but that was the arrangement, wasn't it?'

'Yes it was,' I said, 'and I quite understand. I do hope everything goes well for you. But, if you knew, when I first appeared what you know now, but I had told you that I was a Catholic, would you have turned me down?'

He looked a little sad and pensive. 'Yes, I think I would have to; but

I don't think I can explain it to you. It is deep inside me. I am just glad that you were not Catholic!'

In May 1955 we moved from Church View in Coningsby to Northover, Seel Road, Huyton. It was a modern semi-detached house with a nice small garden front and back. It had been destroyed by bombing in the war, and had been completely rebuilt. As far as we were concerned it was a palace, and for the first few days there we had several giggling fits. At the back of the house, beyond our garden were green fields. We had very few possessions so the move was easily accomplished, and I soon settled down to work. It was quite different: the surgeries were busy and the calls were fewer. The front room of our house had been divided into two small rooms; one as a waiting room and the other as a small consulting room with a desk and a couch; quite adequate for a branch surgery.

Huyton had been a small village a few miles from the edge of Liverpool. After the war, the bomb damaged areas in the city: the slums, with their back-to-back housing, in mean narrow streets, outside toilets and communal water taps in the street, were demolished. New estates were built on the land on the outskirt of the city. New streets with rows and rows of council houses. New communities were settled there out of the central areas of Liverpool, not always happily because in many cases community life was disrupted.

There were two distinct groups in the Huyton area. The new arrivals, essentially Liverpudlians living in the new estates, and the old Huytonians who still referred to Huyton as a village and who kept their distance from the new arrivals. Within two hundred yards of our house there was a council house estate: called the Hagg Estate. All the roads were named after Labour politicians: Attlee Road, Lansbury Road, Hardy Road; and running alongside the estate a main thoroughfare: Wilson Road. It was from this estate that most of the people using my surgery came. They were nearly all from Liverpool, re-settled in Huyton.

The first thing that I noticed when I came to the house was a strong chemical smell. Not unpleasant but quite pungent. I asked what it was.

'It is the smell of the wire enamelling process that is done in the BICC wire producing company in Huyton Quarry.' I was told. British Insulated Calendar Cables was a very large factory employing a large local work force. Huyton Quarry was the part of Huyton where most of the working men lived; as opposed to Huyton village that was a more residential area. The smell of the enamelling did not worry us, it was not unpleasant and we soon got used to it. But it reminded us very clearly of our time there when we returned to Huyton some 30 years later on a short visit, the smell produced a very vivid memory of the past.

Dr Garson's consulting room was the front room of his house in Bluebell Lane. There, Charles and I held the surgery on alternate days. When I was there, he would service the branch surgery at my house in Seel Road. The attendance at Bluebell Lane was much greater than at Seel Road; a few came from the village areas, but most from the big estates north of the Prescot Road: Longview, Woolfall Heath and Knowsley.

Every so often, and quite frequently a salesman from one of the big drug companies, would be waiting their turn to see the doctor and they would be doing their best to persuade us GPs to use their brands of medicines. The use of synthetic drugs manufactured by the drug companies was on the increase, as opposed to the alkaloids, that is drugs extracted from natural sources like belladonna and digitalis. These synthetics carried the name given by the manufacturer. So if the doctor prescribed Chloramphenicol, an antibiotic made by Parke Davis, the patient would have to be given the proprietary Parke Davis product and not the so called generic form of Chloromycetin which was cheaper and could be made by any company once the patent had expired. The government soon realised this and insisted that where there was a generic substitute, the doctor must use this form in the interest of economy.

I was sitting in the surgery one morning when a salesman from Distillers Company came in to see me. As soon as he entered, he placed a little white plastic box in front of me. 'Here you are, doctor. Distaval, the first safe, non barbiturate sleeping tablet and drug to control morning sickness in your pregnant patients.' The box remained where it was and I never used it, thank goodness. It was in fact Thalidomide – and we all know what devastating Teratogenic results that it produced in babies whose mothers had taken it to cure their sickness in pregnancy. Absence or deformity of limbs called Phocomelia. One cannot be too cautious with new drugs, as the old saying went: 'Be not the first by whom the new is tried, nor yet the last to cast the old aside!'

The major drug companies liked to get the GPs in an area together to advertise new products by using visual aids and free samples. The only way to ensure that doctors would attend such functions was to invite them to a free dinner. A fairly new salesman in the area on one occasion, was not sure which venue to use for this purpose. So he asked a young GP for advice.

'Oh' said the young man, 'we GPs are a bit fed up with the run of places you guys are taking us for a meal. Why don't you take us somewhere different?'

'Where would you suggest?' asked the salesman.

'Oh, why not try the Sharrow Bay restaurant?' This was indeed a very special place. I went to that meeting and it was a very special meal indeed. So was the bill when the company paid it. I am told that a copy was pasted to the wall in the company offices as a warning to representatives to 'go easy'.

I hadn't been living in Seel Road very long before I was consulted by a patient, a lady from Attlee Road. She came in with her daughter, a child of about four years old.

'Can I have a sustificate for me husband. He's off work and he needs one for the health and a private one for work.'

'Well, I'm sorry I can't possibly give him a medical certificate unless I have seen him. Why can't he come to the surgery?'

'He's got a bad back, it's all that lifting he has to do at work. The foreman said that if he doesn't send a note in he'll get the sack!' said she.

'That seems a bit hard,' said I. 'Where does he work?'

'He's a hod carrier out at Kirby on the building site there. He's got to send a sustificate, and I want a note for sick pay from the Health 'an all!'

'All right, I'll call in and see him and examine him after the surgery. Where do you live?'

'Number 5 Attlee Road. But it's no good you coming now, he's not there!'

'Well where is he then?'

'He's gone down to T. J. Hughes to get a new coat, he won't be back 'till tea time.'

'Well, if he can go down to Liverpool, he could come here, so please tell him to come to the surgery tonight or tomorrow, and I'll see him.'

'He'll be mad, I tell you. He said he had to have the notes today.' She left without another word but as she was going out, I heard her say to her daughter: 'He won't give me the bloody sustificate; he's a bugger!'

Later that week, she had to come again to the surgery, again with her daughter about something else. But as she came in, the little girl looked at me and exclaimed, 'Boocca, Boocca, Boocca!' I didn't understand at first what she was trying to say then it dawned on me!

Meanwhile we had to think about finding a school for our elder daughter. She would be five next birthday. We called in at St Michael's Church School in the village. It had a very good reputation and we met Miss Critchley, one of the teachers.

'I am so sorry,' she said. 'We are absolutely full. We cannot possibly take any more children for next year. I'm afraid that Mrs Barlow, the headmistress is away. She's not well. You could call again when she returns and speak to her. Perhaps you should consider one of the other local schools.' She named a number of other primary schools in the area. But Marjorie and I just didn't fancy any of them. It so happened that we took a call the next day from Mr Jack Barlow.

'Could the doctor please call to see my wife, she's ill in bed with a fever.'

'You go' said Charles to me. 'It's on your way home; Hazel Bank, Huyton Hey road. If Jack Barlow isn't there, his father will let you in, he's staying there at the moment I believe.'

I called after surgery on my way home and an elderly man opened the door.

'Come in,' he said, 'you're the new doctor aren't you? Edith is upstairs, she's not been well for a day or two. I'll show you where her bedroom is.'

'Mrs Barlow was lying in her bed not looking at all cheerful.

'Hello, I'm Dr Frost-Smith, how can I help you – what seems to be the trouble?'

She explained to me that she felt unwell and described the various symptoms from which she was suffering. I discussed it with her and explained the treatment that I thought would be effective.

'I think a short course of antibiotics will cure the infection and do the trick,' said I.

We talked for a while and she asked me if we had children.

'Yes we have a baby girl aged two and a daughter aged five next birthday. I really wanted to send her to your school: St Michael's in Derby Road. I understand it is a church school and I am a communicating church member; but I understand that you are full.'

'We're always overflowing' she said, 'but I think we will find room for your daughter. Will you bring her along to see me next week when I shall be back at work, if your tablets work!'

'I'm sure they will,' I said. 'I'll pop in to see you in two days to make sure, and thank you.' What a relief to have got that settled, I thought, Marjorie will be pleased.

The practice at Huyton was not large. There were about ten GPs in the area and there was competition to attract patients because the income of practices still, as before, depended almost entirely on the number of patients registered with the practice. There were payments for some extra services like maternity care and for immunising the children but apart from these, there were, as I   remember, no added fees for other services such as minor operations. Most of my visiting was around the four large council house estates, but I did have some patients in the older part of Huyton. These were patients who had lived in the area since 1940 or earlier, mostly in their own houses. But I had only a handful of families from the original village who had been living there before the 1939-45 war. There was a well established medical practice that had catered for these older residents for many years.

In my duties in the surgery, and in visiting patients at home, most of the work consisted in looking after a mixture of middle to working class families. The biggest change for me was that it was not a dispensing practice. At that time nearly all dispensing practices were small. They might employ a receptionist but very often the doctor's wife would do that job. Most doctors working in rural areas or in smaller urban areas used their own premises as consulting rooms. However, more and more GPs were beginning to form partnerships working together as a group from rented premises used exclusively as a medical centre. I believe that in all cases the practices were not reimbursed by the government for practise expenses because GPs had negotiated a contract that classed them as independent contractors. Doctors were not then, and still are not salaried workers. When doctors could be persuaded to work together in harmony with each other, they could cover each other so that they could take time off, knowing that their patients were attended to by a trusted colleague.

Soon changes in the contract allowed doctors to employ paid ancillary staff for which there was limited reimbursement. Then health centres began to appear for the use of which GPs paid rent. The use of a health centre enabled GPs to live away from their place of work. It did however take away their complete independence.

Number 79 Bluebell Lane, next door to the surgery, was occupied by an elderly widow. Eventually she decided to move to a bungalow and her house was put on the market. Charles was keen to acquire the property to open it as the main surgery. But in a canny way he did not approach her but instead arranged for a third party to buy the house on his behalf. I think he felt sure that if she knew he wanted the house, the price would go up. The ruse worked; but when the lady found out what he had done she was considerably put out. We transferred all surgery equipment to next door and that freed up Number 81 as Charles and Joyce's home. I now had my own room in which to consult patients. The small kitchen next to my room was an office in which all the records were kept.

My work as a GP in Huyton was no doubt very similar to what went on in any other small urban two man practice. The fewer the number of doctors working together, the more harmonious the relationships between them was likely to be. Members of large practices of six or more partners tended to encounter disagreements with their colleagues. I have met several young GPs who have been unhappy in their work because of this friction. On the other hand, at the time of which I am writing, out of hours call services had not yet come into being. The early out of hours service that I encountered were not at all popular with patients. A person who is ill or distressed wants to see a familiar doctor from his or her practice. The only way to achieve this is by GPs working together in partnerships of two or more. Single handed practices were disappearing fast except in isolated areas like the Hebridean Islands.

I was doing my usual surgery one morning in Seel Road. It was near the end of the morning and I had seen all the patients. There was no one left in the waiting room. A knock came at the door and a lady came in. She was looking stressed. I had seen her about the village and I was aware that she worked in the local telephone exchange, at that time the exchange was manual in Huyton: there was no direct dialling system.

'Good Morning, what can I do for you?' I asked.

She was a rather tall and imposing lady and replied: 'I've got very severe abdominal pain and backache, I can hardly walk.'

'What is your name?' I asked. 'I don't think we have met before. Do you live in Huyton?'

'Yes I live at 24 Longview Drive, and I am Miss Anne Herlow.'

'What is your work, Miss Herlow, and how long have you had this pain?'

'I am the supervisor at the local telephone exchange. I seem to have been going downhill for several weeks. I had to give up today, I really can't manage to go on like this.'

'Let me have a look at you, can you climb up on the couch?'

It was immediately obvious when I felt her abdomen that she was pregnant! Further more that she was at, or almost at term.

'Miss Herlow, you are pregnant and you are in labour. Why did you not say?'

She tried to sit up and flopped back on the couch. 'That is impossible,' she said. 'I cannot be!'

Who is this lady, I wondered, where has she been all her life?

I tried to examine her further and found it difficult, but the baby's head had almost fully dilated the cervix. She was about to enter the second stage of labour. Yet almost impossibly she professed ignorance of the fact that she was pregnant.

'Miss Herlow, you are pregnant and you will soon be delivered of the baby. Do you not remember having sexual intercourse?'

She was almost frantic: 'Yes, but we took precautions, we always do; I cannot be pregnant!'

I listened to the foetal heart and it was normal. Everything else was normal.

'I will have to send for an ambulance to get you into a maternity unit at once.'

'Oh my God, what am I going to do? I can't face this. The father of this child and I are going to be married, but he knows nothing about this.'

I phoned for an emergency ambulance and gave the ambulance office the details. 'I will contact Whiston Hospital Maternity Unit and alert them. Please collect this patient as quickly as you can, because she is in the second stage of labour and I am sure that you don't want to do a delivery in the ambulence.'

'We're on our way,' said the operator.

Miss Herlow arrived at Whiston Maternity Unit in time, she was delivered of a fine baby boy weighing eight pounds.

Of course I followed her up post-natally, and I was pleased that the family, and the father of the baby rallied around her and it all ended happily. But can you believe that a woman of 38 could be unaware in that way?

Charles and I got on very well together. He was a very calm, even tempered man. He worked for and achieved a London MRCP, and that was very unusual for a GP. He offered me a partnership in the practice after about six months, and I was very pleased to accept. The financial terms were quite usual at the time: starting with a one third share of the practice income and rising by very easy stages over a period of eight or nine years to a 49/51% division. That was acceptable then, but not in today's agreements. During the late 1960s a common agreement would be to offer the incoming doctor a salary for the first year and then equal shares. I was happy enough though and soon the situation changed.

Marjorie's parents were very friendly with Mr and Mrs Peel who lived nearby. Jim Peel was the manager of the local Lucas factory at Broadgreen. Their part-time doctor resigned and Jim very kindly offered me the job. It simply consisted of attending the factory on two afternoons a week; I had a consulting room in the sick bay and there were nursing staff. I was asked to examine prospective employees to make sure they were fit for the type of work they would be doing, also to advise on any medical matters that arose between my visits. I really liked this job and routinely went around the factory floor examining with interest all the engineering processes that went on and getting to know the foremen and toolmakers.

After a year or two, Lucas expanded their presence on Merseyside by opening three other factories. One very large one at Fazakerley, a smaller factory at Kirby and a biggish factory at Bromborough on the Wirral, making the Railway Disc Brake. I attended all of them and carried out the same work as medical advisor.

Word gets around and I was soon asked to attend a new factory, nothing to do with the Lucas set up. Fisher Bendix, also in Kirby; they manufactured the Bendix washing machine and the Moulton bicycle as well as many other components produced by their gigantic hydraulic presses. I asked Charles if he would share the work and he agreed. We shared the income from these ventures half and half! I was on good terms with all the directors of Lucas in Birmingham and paid frequent visits there. I also frequently met, and got to know the chief medical officer, Dr Sam Lawson. He retired in the late 1960s and I was offered his job. I thought I was not suitable having no qualifications in Industrial Medicine, it was a big job. The director of personnel said that the company would want me to attend a course in London to obtain a Diploma in Industrial Health before being appointed.

I thought long and hard: it was not what I wanted. I would have to live in Birmingham and spend most of my life in the factory, apart from visiting the many other Lucas establishments around the country monitoring any medical problems and helping with advice. The financial advance would be very significant and the pension prospects great! But I decided that I could not be content with that sort of career. Without much delay, I thanked the Lucas directors and turned the offer down on the basis that my life was destined to work in General Practice, if possible in the country. I have never regretted that decision.

The patients attending the Huyton surgeries were much the same as at most small practices. But Liverpool was noted for the high incidence of chest disease, no doubt due to the heavy pollution of the atmosphere with dust, industrial chemical contamination and a moist atmosphere. The fogs we experienced were exceptionally severe and I sometimes managed to drive into lamp posts or a pillar box because I just could not see one yard ahead! I remember it was often discussed which factor most contributed to cancer and chest disease generally: smoking cigarettes or living in the industrial areas heavy with irritant particles in the atmosphere.

There was a chest clinic at the bottom of Bluebell Lane run by Dr Ross, a respiratory diseases consultant who provided an enormous amount of valuable advice and help at short notice.

One day, a lady came in to see me. She was well dressed and of ample proportions. She looked at me rather severely.

'Young man, are you the doctor?'

'Yes,' I replied, 'how can I help you?'

'Why isn't Dr Garson here? I want to see him about reducing my weight. I've put on two stones in weight this year.'

'I'm sorry he's not in this morning, it's my turn to see the patients and do the surgery.'

'Well can you give me something to make me lose some weight? I can't get into my usual clothes.'

'What do you think that I can give you that will do that for you?'

'You're the doctor, so what do you think?'

I weighed her and she was over twelve stone and she was only five foot three inches tall. Her blood pressure was much higher than it should have been for her age. She had marked ankle swelling. Otherwise, on examination there were no obvious abnormalities.

'You certainly do need to diet and lose some weight' said I.

'Rubbish, young man. I have been dieting now for several weeks and my weight, has if anything risen. Can't you give me some tablets to curb my appetite? My sister takes some yellow tablets, I think they're called Dexedrine.'

'Mrs Watkins, if you take Dexedrine they will act for two or three weeks and maybe lose you a little weight, then they will stop working, and you will put the pounds back on again; but you could become addicted to the tablets and if you continue to use them they will make you ill. What happened to your sister?' I asked.

'Oh, I'm not sure but she has had to go into hospital for treatment for a nervous breakdown.'

'Well there you are,' said I triumphantly. 'Dexedrine is probably responsible for that, and it could happen to you. So my advice to you is that if you want to lose weight, the only safe way is by taking a strict diet. I will give you a diet sheet that will explain it all. But remember: dieting is a way of life not a quick fix. You stick to the principal advice given on that sheet and, over a decent period it will work!'

I don't think that she believed me and I have to confess that to lose weight by dieting is, for some people extremely difficult. I had many encounters with patients, mostly women seeking to improve their figure, and looking for a quick remedy.

There was a growing demand for amphetamines, 'Purple Hearts', Drinamyl and other similar drugs. But I did not have to deal with problems relating to heroin or cocaine addiction. That would come much later, but I was only indirectly concerned.

I was consulted by many young men, mostly students with requests for these stimulant drugs. One evening a well dressed older man came to the surgery. He said that he lived in Birkenhead and was staying with his son for three days locally. He wanted to sign on as a temporary resident and having done that, he said he had run out of his Nembutal sleeping capsules. Would I give him a prescription for more, he asked.

'Certainly' I said.' I'll write a prescription for ten capsules. That will tide you over until you get home.'

He was obviously very annoyed. 'My doctor usually writes me a 'script for 60, why can't you do the same?'

I explained that he was not known to me and that I was only doing what was recommended. He didn't like it and left in a 'huff' taking with him the prescription for the ten capsules. That was the end of that, or nearly! About a week later I was phoned by the assistant manager of the Liverpool Executive Council. He explained in a friendly way that he had had a complaint from a Mr Tell who was chairman of the Health Committee of Liverpool Corporation. He had complained that I had refused to repeat a prescription that his doctor normally gave him, and that he had run short of the medication when he was away from home. I told the manager that in my opinion I had done the right thing and that nothing would persuade me to do otherwise. 'For all I knew he might be an addict,' I said. He had to agree with me and said that he would smooth it over, and thanked me.

At that time it was very common to take Nembutal as a sleeping tablet. It is a barbiturate and doctors were being advised to use it sparingly; firstly because it is addictive and secondly because habitual use makes it ineffective. There is also a suicide risk. The use of sedatives that are long acting can contribute to accidents, especially in older people.

A policeman phoned and asked me to visit his wife who was ill in bed suffering from bronchitis. They had a house in Knowsley. I called in later that morning and when I knocked, the door was opened by the policeman himself. A Chief Inspector from the police headquarters at Widnes. He showed me up to the bedroom and introduced me to his wife explaining that I was the doctor.

'Hello Mrs Gunn, what can I do for you?'

'It's my chest doctor, I have this terrible cough and it's been going on all night. I've got pains in my chest every time I cough or take a deep breath. I've nearly driven my husband mad with the coughing and I'm coughing up some foul yellow sputum. I feel awful.'

I examined her chest and there were marked signs of an active infection with crepitations at the bases. There was no evidence of any consolidation in the lungs. She had a fever of 100° Fahrenheit and looked ill. I checked her other systems and found nothing else.

'As you said Mrs Gunn you have acute bronchitis and you need a course of antibiotics.'

I gave her husband a prescription for Terramycin and said I would call in two days. I did call on the second day and again was let into the house by Mr Gunn.

'It's magical,' he said, 'she's a whole lot better. You go up and see her.'

It was indeed so, Mrs Gunn's fever had subsided and she was a whole lot better, sitting up and reading.

'Thank you so much' said Chief Inspector Gunn. 'Please let me know if I can help you in any way.'

As it happened, I asked for his help sooner than I had thought I would: quite soon! I was returning to the surgery late after attending a factory clinic at Kirby when I was stopped in a built up area by a policeman with a speed camera. I was travelling, he said at 42 miles per hour in an area with a speed limit of 30. I explained that I was on duty and late, but he told me he had to report the incident. If I was unhappy about it I could to write in to the headquarters at Widnes, but he could do nothing, he had to report the event. I telephoned Chief Inspector

Gunn and explained what had happened.

'Were you on duty doctor?' he asked.

'Yes' I replied and outlined the situation.

'That's all right then' he said, 'you'll just get a written warning letter, but be careful in future.'

Now I owe him one and it wasn't long in arriving!

'Doctor Frost-Smith' said the voice on the 'phone. 'Chief Inspector Gunn would like a word, shall I put him through?'

'Doctor,' said the Chief Inspector. 'We need a police doctor in the area of your practice and I would like you to consider taking it on. It's just a part time commitment. You would be called upon to give advice on an ad hoc basis, Possibly to advise in the case of a driver who is arrested on suspicion of driving with excess alcohol. You would need to examine the patient and decide whether he or she should be charged.'

'Thanks for the offer, but I don't really want that sort of work.'

'Please consider it carefully, we need your help in this matter,' he said.

After much persuasion over the next week or so I found myself having to agree to do the job. Soon I was telephoned by a senior police doctor in Manchester who outlined my duties. It scared me stiff! He explained that following my agreement to charge the defendant there would be a court case and I would be cross-examined by a clever barrister who, would tear me to shreds if I had omitted any relevant test. These were the days before the breathalyser. It was not at all cut and dried.

It was of course possible to arrange a blood alcohol test, but the delay could affect the evidence. So a great deal depended on the advice given by the examining doctor at the time the person was arrested. It was not long before I was summoned to Huyton Police Station at two o'clock one morning.

'Is that Dr Frost-Smith,' said a heavy stern voice. 'This is Sergeant Pollard at Huyton Police Station. We have arrested a woman whom we think has been in charge of a motor vehicle while under the influence of alcohol. Can you attend please to examine the suspect?'

'Where is the patient, er – suspect?'

'We are holding the woman under arrest at the Police Station in

Derby Road.'

I sighed. I knew it would come to this. 'Yes, I'll be with you in fifteen minutes.'

When I entered the police station I was guided to a room where a woman of about fifty years old sat with a woebegone fearful expression on her face, sitting on a bench in the room.

'Will you examine this person doctor and when you have decided whether we should charge her, please come in to the office to complete the required form.' They left us alone together.

I asked her for her name and age and I performed a quick examination; it was after all two o'clock in the morning. I took her blood pressure, her temperature and an assessment of her cardiovascular system and her nervous system. I found no abnormalities. Incidentally I had no chaperone provided to be with me while examining a female patient.

'What happened to you?' I asked.

She looked miserable and tearful. 'I was parked outside Walton Hospital waiting for my husband to turn up, and by mistake, I leant on the horn button. Within seconds a policeman put his head through the car window.

'He said "You're smelling of alcohol madam. Have you been drinking?"

'I did have a glass of whisky an hour ago.

"I'm arresting you on suspicion of being in charge of this car while under the influence of alcohol."

'I wasn't even driving the wretched car, I was just waiting for my husband; but he said I was technically in charge of the vehicle and he brought me here. I have been charged with the offence.'

There was a straight white line running the length of the room.

'Will you please walk along this line with you arms folded in front of you?'

She did so, and walked as straight as an arrow. She stood on one leg with hardly any wobble. Her speech was clear and normal, not slurred. I made my decision and entered the office. The sergeant, a great bulky red faced man, looked at me accusingly.

'Well?' he enquired.

'I think she is fit to drive and not under the influence of alcohol. You cannot charge her,' I said with a quake in my voice.

'WHAT!' he shouted. 'Would you let her drive you home?'

'Certainly, in my opinion she is fit to drive.'

I left at about 3.30am. They never asked me again, thank goodness! I never spoke again to the chief inspector and I was not again stopped for speeding until years later, in Dumfries.

I never really settled in Huyton but we couldn't move while our children were on the verge of 'O' and 'A' level school exams. I thought lovingly of buying a cottage in the country somewhere. Some new cottages were being built at Chapel Stile near Skelwith Bridge on the road to Langdale – a real beauty spot. I rang the agent. He said that I could reserve one of the cottages by sending him a deposit of £50.

'No,' said Marjorie very firmly. 'If you want to be in the country then we must go and live and work there.'

That settled it. I wrote to the executive councils in Carlisle, Kendal, Cheshire and Shropshire asking if they knew of any practices wanting a partner. I received several replies and followed them all up.

One day when I was in my consulting room in Huyton, I was visited by the Regional Medical Officer, Dr Alan Judson. This was quite a usual routine visit. His job was to make sure that there were no problems in the practice and that my prescribing was reasonable. When we started talking I found that he had been in practice in a village called Shap in Westmorland. Everyone had heard tell of Shap, the stiff climb up Shap Fell from Kendal and the wintry conditions that prevailed in the region. He told me that the Shap doctor in the 1930s had been a Dr Prentice. He had either retired or died at the end of the 1939 war and Alan had taken his place as Shap GP. There was no doubt that he and his family had enjoyed living there.

After he retired from Shap he had worked as Regional Medical Officer and he just happened to visit my practice in that capacity. He told me all about his life as a GP in Shap. He and his family had lived in The Hermitage, a very beautiful old house, and he practised and held his surgeries there. The tales he told me of his being a doctor there filled me with a longing to move to a similar area. So when one evening some time later I was telephoned by a Dr Blue of Orton in Cumbria saying that he had been informed that I was looking for an opening in General

Practice, I was quite thrilled. He said that one of the partners in the practice was leaving and they were looking for a replacement.

'Are you interested?' he asked. I said that I was, very interested and he invited Marjorie and me to his house in Orton, near Shap where we could talk about it. We received a warm welcome from him, his wife, Joanne and Dr Cranston, one of the partners in the practice.

After exchanging the details of what their practice wanted and what I was looking for, we were shown the house in Little Strickland that I would possibly like to buy if we decided to accept the offer. The present incumbent in the partnership, a Dr Derek Cowan wanted to move to an area where his wife Elizabeth would be happier. I had several meetings with Derek Cowan, he told me that Elizabeth did not like living in the country and they were in the process of moving to an urban practice in Yorkshire.

I had made up my mind. I wrote to Dr Ian Blue saying I would like to join the partnership if they would have me. I received a very warm and friendly letter in return, welcoming me and suggesting a starting date in November 1971. That would be ideal as there would then be a gap of just five weeks between Derek Cowan leaving and my starting. All of this happened in early summer 1971. I had to give three months notice to the executive council and to Charles Garson. He was naturally a little upset, but then he was in his early seventies and was going to retire very soon. I really could not stay any longer. I was set on a move to the country and the Shap practice was just what I was looking for. I was also really keen on working in a dispensing practice, though things had changed greatly since my days in Coningsby.

We investigated the availability of houses to buy, but the large house that I had noticed that had been the GP's residence for some years back: The Hermitage, was now owned by another family. Eventually we bought The Long House from the Cowan family.

12
Cumbria Country Practice

I arrived in Shap on the 19 November 1971, having completed the sale of Overleigh, our house in Huyton and closed the house. Marjorie had already arrived and was staying temporarily in a cottage at Robinson Trees opposite Simpsons Garage. That first day when I arrived and viewed the village and the surrounding countryside I felt a big thrill, just like the thrill I felt when I arrived at Coningsby in 1953, and very similar to the time in 1939 when we came to live in Wales.

The surgery was basically a small bungalow with minor alterations so that it was suitable to use as a surgery. The practice had paid £4,000 for it in 1968 and I was required to buy out Derek Cowan's share. Previously patients had been seen in one of the three cottages in the row called Robinson Trees.

Patients did not have to make an appointment to see the doctor but they had to come at surgery time: 9-10 am, or 5-6 pm in the evening. The surgeries however always finished about an hour after the scheduled time.

There has never been, in all the practices in which I have worked, an appointment system; patients came, and waited their turn to see the doctor. Of course, in a very big practice, or in hospital clinics, especially nowadays, an appointment system is essential. But it is in some senses a modern innovation necessary to deal with large numbers. I remember that in the Royal Infirmary in Cardiff, where I trained to be a doctor, there was a large outpatient hall, and patients could just turn up and wait to see the specialist they needed, free of charge, even before the NHS started; I think I remember correctly.

Formal visits to a specialist would often be in the consultant's own home and prior to the NHS the patient would have to pay the fee! I spoke on one occasion to a GP, I forget his name, but he had been a pupil of my father in Appleby Grammar School in the early 1900s. He looked at me with some amazement. 'You cannot be a son of Pif Smith,' he said, 'there's a generation missing!' There wasn't a missing generation, it was just that my father was nearly fifty when I was born! He, the doctor, had practised in Orton in the 1930s and patients would, he told me sometimes come to see him at a meal time without warning, any time of day in fact – that is how it was then. Patients many times have told me that even with an appointment, they wait just as long to see their doctor as they did in pre-appointment days. GP appointments benefit the doctor more that the patient. Some patients may need only two or three minutes to conclude their visit, but some may need half an hour. The doctors seem to be able to overcome this difficulty however.

I, like my partners, Dr Blue, Dr Cranston and Dr Brown dispensed for patients at the time of the consultation. I also, like them, dispensed repeat medicines at the time when patients asked for them. I had two part-time receptionists, Mrs Nellie Etheridge who had been with the practice for quite a few years, and Miss Amy Taylor, known to all from long ago as Susan! They had always given out the 'repeat' medicines and I let them continue to do so. Neither had had any training in dispensing, Susan though was an experienced state registered nurse. If they were not sure about any repeat medicine they would ask me, and during the whole time I worked in Shap they never made a mistake, they were so careful.

Shap practice, like many country practices has no easy access to a pharmaceutical chemist. The nearest chemist's shop is in Penrith, some ten miles or so away. It is unreasonable to expect patients to be able to get a prescription given by their doctor in Shap dispensed in Penrith. Nevertheless the pharmaceutical profession has tended to oppose doctors being allowed to dispense. I have attended many meetings where this has been made clear. It is clear and understandable that in remote areas like Shap and Orton the GP must be able to dispense for his patients.

It is not so clear when the practice centre is in an urban area which has a chemist shop. Many patients who live in outlying areas come in to the centre to see the doctor who then provides them with their drugs, although the chemist's shop is nearby. This is understandably a sore point with the chemist in this situation. Some practices are small enough to be unsustainable without the extra income derived from dispensing. One young lady living in Shap who had just qualified in pharmacy told me that her ambition was to set up a chemist's shop in Shap. I told her that if that happened, Shap would be denigrated to a 'call in' branch surgery of a Penrith practice losing its status as a comprehensive medical centre. It was not easy always to obtain supplies of medicines from wholesale companies at the time of which I am writing.

The practice as a whole: Shap, Orton and Kirkby Stephen entered into an agreement with a large wholesale instrument and pharmaceutical supplier in Leeds. Their representative visited us once every two months to receive our orders for supplies to be delivered to Kirkby Stephen, Orton and Shap. The small profits from dispensing increased the practice income sufficiently to make the three practices viable. We had to purchase any shortages arising in the interval before the next supply from Leeds was due, by buying from a local chemist in Penrith.

We were given good terms and friendly service by this local pharmacy: Cowper's Chemist and we would not have been able to manage without their reliable help and cooperation. Nevertheless the generous discounts they allowed us could not match the prices of drugs and medicines obtained directly from wholesalers. So my partners and I had to plan ahead very carefully to avoid running short of necessary supplies.

Patients understandably expected to be given their medicine, even 'repeats' at the time of the consultation, and they nearly always were, but this arrangement would not work today, where the number and variety of treatments have increased. It was beginning to unravel when I retired. Latterly supplies from a Carlisle firm were grudgingly left daily at a collection point and picked up by me on my way to Shap surgery in the afternoon. Visits from the representatives of drugs manufacturers, Burroughs Wellcome, Glaxo and others were many and frequent, trying to persuade me to use their products; but I cannot remember any wholesale suppliers calling, to ask me to buy from them.

The position is different now I expect. I have been told that some pharmacy companies are offering to deliver medicines directly to the patient's door thus excluding the local GP dispensary. Country dispensing practices are often small and over the years, even before the start of the NHS they have in most cases been able to supply a patient's medicine at the time of the consultation. I have worked in two country dispensing practices and they both relied upon the income derived from the dispensing part of the service. If this service were stopped or reduced to any great extent, the viability of the practice as a whole could be threatened. In that event there is no doubt that patients could find themselves having to travel some distance to a larger medical group, or maybe the original practice could become a local branch surgery open only on certain days.

I, and I am sure many GPs are often asked to prescribe a sleeping tablet. We know that if patients take a hypnotic drug regularly they soon become habituated; the drug ceases to produce the same effect. The patient may then ask to be prescribed a bigger dose or a more powerful drug to achieve the same result. In my early years in practice barbiturates were very commonly used to promote sleep in chronic insomniacs, but it was becoming clear that there were many disadvantages. Patients can become addicted: in fact a police report stated in the 1970s that the problem of addiction to barbiturates was greater than the problem of addiction to the harder drugs, at that time. There was also the problem of confusion leading to an elderly patient falling. Access to powerful hypnotics could increase the possibility of suicide in a patient with a mental illness.

The phenothiazines: Librium, Valium, Mogadon, Temazepam and many, many others had not yet arrived. I think that is why the sales representative from Dista was so triumphantly confident when he showed me Distaval.

By the time I arrived in Shap, Mogadon was one of the sedatives of choice. But I soon found that many patients were already hooked on Nembutal, which is quite a powerful barbiturate. I found it extremely difficult to wean these patients off the 'barbs' and on to Mogadon. Some would say: 'out of the frying pan into the fire!'

There were two elderly ladies, sisters, living in an isolated cottage on the fells. They were characters. Both had worked all their lives and were now retired and 'taking it easy'.

'Doctor,' said the elder and more persuasive of the two. 'Can you let us have some more Nembutal?'

'Oh, I don't think that's a good idea. Why d'you want to take them?'

'Well you see,' she said,'Mary and I always sit in our sun room after lunch and relax with a gin and martini and a Nembutal!'

Some of the older recipes for bottles of medicine would certainly not be acceptable today.

Bromides were sometimes added to medicines for chronically ill patients until the early twentieth century and could be bought without a prescription. Paraldehyde was used when I was at Walton Hospital, intramuscularly to restrain a violent patient. My father told me that when he was ten years old he was sent to the pharmacist to buy some laudanum for his younger brother who was suffering from rheumatic fever and had severe joint pain. This drug is extracted from opium and at the time was more or less freely available over the counter. It was there on the shelf in Coningsby Surgery Dispensary as tincture of laudanum.

When I was practising in Huyton, I was advised to prescribe for one of my patients who, admittedly was terminally ill with cancer, the Brompton Cocktail, a powerful medicine containing morphine, cocaine in 98% alcohol and chlorpromazine, (an anti- nauseant)! As a matter of fact, the patient did not die of the cancer, but fell off a ladder and died of a heart attack eventually!

The sedative of choice for children was chloral hydrate; it was said to be safe, but I never had occasion to use it.

I soon fell into the routine, getting to know patients in the villages and in the surrounding area. I did about five home visits each day, and only rarely if there was an epidemic of influenza or measles, might have to do as many as ten. The MMR (measles, mumps and rubella) and the flu vaccine were not as yet available.

Soon after our arrival, there was a smallpox scare in Penrith. No one had been diagnosed with the disease, but there had been a possible contact by a Penrith resident with a case in London. It was advised that any person, including children, who had not already been vaccinated earlier, should be vaccinated as soon as possible.

A clinic was set up in Brunswick Road and the Penrith doctors as a team, carried out mass vaccination on volunteers. It so happened that on that morning I was consulted by a young man who was complaining of a vesicular rash (small blisters) on his hands and arms. This is the area where a smallpox rash is first seen. I had never ever seen a case of smallpox. I wasn't exactly alarmed, but I was determined to take every care. The thought of a smallpox epidemic in Shap spurred me on! I contacted the Westmorland Medical Officer of Health and explained my worry to him. There was instant action: He came up to Shap that morning with an expert in infectious diseases and we all examined the young patient. The verdict from the expert: 'This is not smallpox!' We all sighed with relief and the two medics and I repaired to The Long House for coffee. There were no cases of smallpox found in the Penrith area on that occasion.

In the early summer of 1972, one morning quite early, Sergeant Moore from Shap police station phoned: 'Doctor, there's been an accident at Blea Water Tarn. A party of school boys from a school at Dalston were out walking and climbing in the High Street area. There are, apparently some serious injuries and I have been asked to attend with a doctor. Can you come with me, if so I'll take you to the spot?'

'I'll come and collect you right away,' I replied. I had to leave the morning surgery to attend to this call. This was one of the occasions, of which there were more than one, when Marjorie took the morning surgery. She was quite used to doing surgeries in her work as a locum in Liverpool. That was no problem. But she was not used to dispensing, and my receptionists had to help her out, telling her what medicaments we had, and pointing them out on the shelves. In fact she was far better than I was at listening to patient's problems. Frequently young mothers would call at The Long House to talk to her in order to discuss health problems concerning their children.

Sergeant Moore and I drove to the south end of Haweswater and started the steep walk up the footpath leading to the tarn. I must admit, I was not ideally dressed for fell walking, being a newcomer to the Lake District – also I was clutching my case with most of the implements and drugs that might be needed for a patient at the bedside or in the surgery – not at all for a fellside emergency. As we climbed, we heard the sound of a whistle being blown by someone in the party, to guide us to them. Sergeant Moore answered by blowing the whistle he had brought with him to say that help was on the way. After about 40 minutes we came up to the party. The boys with the master from the Lime House School in Dalston had been attempting to climb a steep face of rock adjacent to Blea Water Tarn. They were all around fourteen to sixteen years old. One boy was clinging to the face of the rock twenty feet or so above the tarn. He was shouting piteously: 'Please help me, someone please help me!'

The sergeant and I looked at each other. There was no way that either of us could attempt to reach him, and the teacher who had brought them, was standing there neither use nor ornament!

'They've sent for the mountain rescue team, apparently,' said Sgt. Moore. 'A boy ran back to the Haweswater Hotel and phoned. That's how I got the message. I think you'd better look at that lad over there, he looks as if he's badly injured.'

I went over to the boy who was lying on his back, groaning and in obvious pain.

'Where does it hurt?' I asked.

'Please help me, for God's sake give me something to ease the pain. I think both my legs are broken!'

He was certainly right. His left lower leg was at an angle. Obviously a complete fracture with displacement. I tried to make him as comfortable as I could and I gave him an injection of a quarter of a grain of morphine intramuscularly. After a few minutes he relaxed and closed his eyes.

I approached another boy lying still on the shale by the tarn. I was shocked to see that he was dead. The cause of death was immediately obvious. He had a head injury in the temporal region which had been bleeding profusely. He probably had a depressed fracture of his skull; there were other injuries to his arms and legs. He had obviously fallen from a height.

Very soon, the Patterdale Mountain Rescue team appeared, striding up the hill as if they were walking on the level. They had with them stretchers, each on two bicycle wheels. Two of the men climbed up the rock and brought the boy who was clinging there safely down. He had a fractured wrist, and was trembling and pale with shock. The team soon took over and brought all the injured and the dead boy down to the ambulance waiting at the head of the lake.

As we walked down, I spoke with Dr Ogilvie, who acted as the medical officer to the team. He was a GP in Glenridding and was a skilled man dealing with accidents of this kind. He knew the area well.

'They should never have been there,' he said to me. 'That is "rotten rock" and quite unsuitable for climbing. The man must be mad taking the boys there.'

I went to see the lad who had broken his legs, and had been taken to the Cumberland Infirmary. He was making a good recovery. His left leg had a compound fracture with splintering of the bone. It needed a bone graft.

The incident was front page news in the major daily papers, and of course there was an inquest that I had to attend. That would seem to the end of this terrible accident. The poor lad who had been killed was Indian. I met his parents who were of course distraught.

More than a year later I met one of my patients whose son was a pupil at the school. She told me that the teacher who had been in charge of the boys when the accident happened, had gone on an expedition to South America. I was told that he had gone walking in the Andes Mountains and had disappeared; never to be seen again!

We were very happy living in the Long House. It was very old with a date of 1686 on the stone work over the porch door. It had been built by a member of the Betham family who were seventeenth century clerics and writers; one of them was an MP in the parliament that voted to behead Charles I! The house was full of character, it was a lovely family home; but like many old properties it had its faults. Built in the late seventeenth century with walls three feet thick and no damp course, there was a constant battle to keep the rooms dry and warm. Nevertheless, it was a very suitable home to enjoy life with a family while they were growing, also to entertain our larger family at holiday times.

Before long I was contacted about the house by an elderly lady who was my patient and who lived in Shap.

'Have you been in the cellar doctor?' she asked.

'No, I do not think there is a cellar,' I replied.

'I was a maid in the Long House 45 years ago,' she said. 'We kept our coal in the cellar. It was dropped in through an opening from outside. But we entered the cellar through a door in the old kitchen and down three steps. It might have had central heating installed by now. So the cellar would be where the central heating boiler was installed.'

'When I worked there,' she said, 'there were iron rings let into the wall. They were not used in my time, but when the Reivers, the wild lowland Scottish men used to invade the area a long time ago in search of booty, cattle and women to kidnap, any of them that were caught were chained up to those iron rings.'

'Well, I haven't noticed the iron rings but will you come and have a cup of tea with us? You can show us where they were. I'll come and fetch you in the car.'

She came a few days later and I showed her around the house.

'Oh, it has all changed,' she said. 'I hope you don't get any Scottish invaders now, because the iron rings have gone and there's nowhere where you could shackle them!'

'I don't think that the Lowland Scots are going to invade us any more; well not in a physical sense! But the Jacobite Rebellion in which Bonny Prince Charlie fought his way south as far as Derby, until he was repelled by the Duke of Cumberland, retreated though Little Strickland. Some of the Highland officers were billeted here in this village. That is why the house down opposite the church is called the Barracks and some of the Scots stayed here in the Long House. One of them is said to have dropped his silver pistol in the garden. It was taken, so it is said, to the Carlisle Museum. But when I enquired, they said they couldn't find it.'

The Highlanders retreated through Clifton on the A6 near Penrith and that was where the last battle on English soil was fought. There is a plaque in the village commemorating it. I enjoyed meeting this lady whose family had lived just opposite in Ivy Cottage, and worked in the Long House when she was a teenage girl.

'I was employed by Mr Mavie,' she said. 'He was a writer and a gentleman and as such was respected in the village.'

It was very easy to settle in Little Strickland, we were conscious of a warm welcome. I think they liked having the doctor living there. There had been, I am told quite a strong representation by Shap patients who felt that their GP should live locally in Shap village as had been the custom for many years. The Long House was just three miles from the surgery at Shap. As it turned out, the Shap patients found that their access to a doctor was as good as it ever had been.

Our son Paul now aged seven was to attend the village school. We had been in the house only one day, when three or four children called to invite him to join them in play, so he very quickly made new friends. The school was very small. Many years ago in the early 1900s, and until after the second world war when there were more farm workers and bigger families, there were between twenty and thirty pupils. Many of my middle aged patients had attended Little Strickland school later, during the 1930s and 1940s. The small school building had not been big enough and they used the village hall, they called 'The Institute' as an extra classroom and games area. This village hall had been built on land belonging to the Lonsdale Estates and was in the centre of the village. It had one large room, later used by a village badminton club, and a smaller room called the Reading Room, used in recent times for small meetings.

When the Institute was built, just after the First World War, in the 1920s, there was a feeling that people in villages should be given the opportunity and encouragement to read and self educate themselves further, thus adding to the schooling that they already had received. I believe that many similar village halls around the country had this objective in mind when they added a reading room. The Institute in Little Strickland was built by the parish council, or in this case Little Strickland Parish Meeting. Civil parish councils were formed in England under the Reforming Act of 1894. Reading rooms like this would contain newspapers and books for the use of anyone who cared to enjoy the facility. In the 1920s the parish meeting decided to build the Institute. Parish meetings are formed when there are less than 200 electors in the parish; all the electors in the civil parish are entitled to attend and vote.

There is a record in the archives of the official opening of the hall. It was built around a wooden frame clad in corrugated iron. Buildings constructed using these materials have a limited life. It is a great pity that today, at the time of writing, the Institute or village hall is in urgent need of expensive repairs. Grants for this sort of project are available if it can be shown that a community centre has sufficient usage to justify the expense of rebuilding. Most residents think it would be difficult to demonstrate this level of usage.

For the last 60 years, that is within living memory, there were many regular events held in the village: whist drives, parties and some games. The badminton club more recently formed, was very popular among the teenagers. Many other social events were held that were well attended. Now, sadly there is very little demand for the use of the hall for this sort of activity.

Some of my patients, now elderly men told me how they had played around the building during its construction. There was   apparently a great deal of enthusiasm locally to complete the building at that time. The money to build must have been largely donated.

One must remember that most people especially those working in rural areas as well as some of those working in the towns and cities had little opportunity to extend their education after leaving school. The Education Act of 1870 created compulsory education for children under the age of thirteen. Prior to the nineteenth century there were very few schools, most that existed were run by the church, stressing religious education. After the Education Act school boards were set up which could fine parents whose children did not attend. There were exceptions to the law made to cover special circumstances such as children being educated at home or disabled children. At the start of the twentieth century school boards were abolished and replaced by Local Education Authorities. In 1918 the school leaving age was raised to fourteen. It was raised again to fifteen in 1944 near the end of the war, and in 1964 the leaving age was raised again to sixteen.

In 1944 the Butler Act set up the tripartite system: of grammar schools, technical schools and secondary modern schools. The entry into grammar schools and technical schools was determined by the Eleven Plus examination which received then, and still does receive a great deal of criticism especially concerning children who develop later. About this time, bursaries and grants became available to enable children who had achieved the appropriate standard to go to university, regardless of whether funding was available from home.

I have known many elderly patients, who had been born towards the end of the nineteenth century, or early in the twentieth century, particularly those who lived in large towns and cities who, although being intelligent and ambitious, spent their lives working in jobs unsuitable to their level of intelligence. In today's world, such men and women would attend university and achieve much more during their lives. If one can believe Mrs Gaskell the novelist, who wrote in the nineteenth century: if an employer interviewed a prospective employee applying for a servant's job who was well educated enough so that he or she could read and write, the applicant was unlikely to be appointed!

In 1971, when we arrived, there was just one teacher in the Little Strickland school, a very gifted lady who had from eight to twelve pupils, in an age range of five to eleven. As well as the basic education syllabus normally covered in primary schools, they were given an insight into their environment and social studies. They were taught self reliance and care in the community and respect for their neighbours. Paul told me, as did others who had attended that school that the broad social education they received benefited them greatly in later life.

On one occasion, when the schoolmistress was away attending a course, a supply teacher had been organised to take over for about a week. All was going well until one morning, the supply teacher, a Mrs Hopkins phoned Marjorie to say that one of her own children was ill and that she had to remain at home until the doctor arrived.

She asked Marjorie if she would kindly go down to the school for a short while to make sure that all was well until Mrs Hopkins arrived. Marjorie went immediately, it was just time when the school should start. She found somewhat to her surprise that the eldest girl had taken the assembly and prayers, set all the children in their places and given them some appropriate work to do. Marjorie was quite amazed to find that all the children were quietly occupied. That was the sort of responsible relationship among the pupils that was natural in that school.

Unfortunately the small size of the school made it a target for closure. The Cumbria Education Committee wanted to close it, saying that such a small, one teacher school could not provide an ideal primary education. All the parents of pupils, past and present disagreed heartily with that judgement. We all fought vigorously, maintaining that pupils in the Little Strickland school received a primary education that was as good as, or better than average; but it was to no avail and the school closed in 1975 and left a gap in the community. As with many villages the closure of the school, the Greyhound pub, and the village shop, run by Mrs Furness, also contributed to the diminution of communal village life.

The church in the village: St Mary's Thrimby, had been situated at Thrimby, an adjacent village, or township as it had been called, just half a mile away. But in 1815 the church was moved in its entirety to Little Strickland in order to release land to the Lowther Estates and bring the church into a more central and accessible position. Marjorie and I attended Thrimby Church fairly regularly, we enjoyed very much the lasting friendships that attending services engendered.

The church itself is most interesting from the point of view that it still has evidence of the character of the old Chapel of Ease that had box pews with the names of the families who owned the right to sit in the pews engraved in the woodwork. There is also a large old piece of sandstone let into the wall of the porch with the following inscription. The wall was very damp and we brought the slab of stone back into the church.

THE THRIMBY INSCRIPTION
EXPRIMIT. UNDE. DEI. LAUDES. LOCUS. HICCE. BEATUS?
QUIS. DEDIT. HUIC. FORMAN. QUI. MODO. PULVIS. ERAT?
ARMIGER. EFFECIT. FLETCHAR. STRICKLANDICUS.
OLIM PRAESIDIUM. PATRIAE. LEGIBUS.
ALTUS. HONOS. QUI. FUIT.
OBIIT. FATIS. CONCEDIMUS. OMNES;
FATA. AT. NULLA. PREMANT. HOC. PIETATIS. OPUS.
TD   LD   1695   LS

In 1686 Thomas Fletcher of Strickland restored Thrimby Chapel, which for many years had stood in the field opposite the present houses called Chapel View, as a Chapel-of-Ease to the parish church at Morland. In 1695 the Rev. Lancelot Sisson, curate of Thrimby composed the Latin verses above to commemorate the restoration.

In 1815 when the present church of St Mary, Thrimby was built, the inscribed stone was transferred here and incorporated in the wall of the porch. The following is a translation by the Rev. Joseph Whiteside, son of the Rev. Stephen Whiteside, perpetual curate of Thrimby from 1859 to 1865:-

How comes this House of Prayer to declare the praise of God?
Who has restored the dilapidated fabric?
It was the work of Fletcher Esquire, recently of Strickland.
A bulwark of his fatherland, an ornament of the law,
Who alas is dead; we all submit to the fates,
But may no fate efface his labour of love.

I kept one room in the Long House, the entrance hall at the south end of the building as a place where patients could come by arrangement in an emergency. Quite frequently, often in the evenings, but sometimes at midday, when the surgery in Shap was closed, a patient would telephone me at home and ask if they could see me concerning a mild emergency. The patient would often be a worried parent with a sick child. In addition to this, mothers often 'phoned in the morning just before school:

'John says he doesn't feel well enough to go to school, he does look a bit pale, can I bring him to you. I don't know whether to make him go or not?'

Such situations were usually resolved very quickly and really saved time both for patients and for me.

Frequently farmers would come with problems such as having stood on a nail that had penetrated their boot. They would ask if they needed an anti-tetanus injection. It reminded me that farm workers in my uncle's farm used to wear hob nailed boots. A nail could not penetrate the sole of such footwear. Today, wellington boots are nearly always the footwear of choice among farmers; a nail will penetrate the sole, but water will not!

A deep penetrating wound from a nail that had possibly been in the soil or manure could cause tetanus. Farmers knew this well enough and although most had had active immunisation as children it was considered wise to administer a 'booster' to reinforce the patient's immunity.

One lunchtime I got a different call; a much more serious accident had occurred. The caller was a young lad and he sounded desperate and frightened.

'Doctor, it's Colin Johnson speaking. Can you come at once please: it's my dad, he's been badly hurt. He's out in the field by the house, he's lying there on the ground. We've been muck spreading, and I think he's seriously injured. Please can you come quickly?' He named the farm, it was in the Crosby Ravensworth area about five miles away and I knew it well.

'I'm on my way,' said I. I grabbed my two bags: one of them containing injections and diagnostic instruments and the other with dressings and suturing material. Armed with these I wasted no time and drove to the farm where the patient was lying. As soon as I stopped in the yard

I could see where the accident had happened. The giant muck spreader and the tractor were stationary in the middle of the field next to the house. I could see Barnet Johnson lying quite still by the side of the machine, his son Colin kneeling beside him. It had been raining heavily and the ground was slippery. I managed to hurry across the uneven wet ground but it took me a few minutes to reach the two of them.

Barnet was a very likeable man. I had had many conversations with him in the past and I found him very supportive and always ready to share a joke. There was the occasion when Marjorie had asked me to attend a local auction sale of furniture being held in one of the houses in Crosby Ravensworth.

I had not lived in the area very long and so I didn't know many of the men and women attending the sale. There was one particular item of furniture for which Marjorie had asked me to bid. It was an antique corner cupboard. The bidding commenced, one or two ladies present bidding against each other. I put in a bid, really the most that I wanted to pay. Immediately I was overbid by someone present. I cannot go much further I thought, when Barnet called out: 'Shut up! Can't you see the doctor wants it!'

I bid again, and there was silence, no more bids. Nobody commented, not even the auctioneer! So I came away with my prize, thanks to Barnet. I think of him every time I open the door of that cupboard.

Now approaching the muck spreader and the form of Barnet lying face downwards on the muddy ground, with Colin kneeling beside him. I could see that poor Barnet was dead. I checked his pulses, but there was no sign of a heart beat.

'I am really sorry Colin, I am afraid your dad has passed away.' Poor Colin was devastated with tears streaming down his face.

'I must phone for an ambulance,' I said, 'in the meantime, we must cover him with a coat.'

Jane, his wife came hurrying across towards us.

'What has happened?' she shouted. 'Oh my God, is he hurt? Oh for God's sake what has happened?'

I took her arm. 'I am very sorry Jane, Barnet has had an accident, I am sorry to say that he is dead.' Poor Jane, she was kneeling beside him sobbing.

'Come Colin, we must take your mum back to the house and phone for help.'

The ambulance came eventually and Barnet was taken to the Cumberland Infirmary to assess his injuries. There would have to be a post mortem and an inquest to determine exactly what had happened. After a little while, when Colin and his mother had settled down, I spoke to Colin.

'Tell me what happened,' I asked.

'We were spreading muck in the field, I was sitting beside Dad on the tractor when the outlet blocked and the manure stopped spraying. Before I could stop him he had jumped off the tractor and run round to the back to clear the blockage. He did that while we were still moving. It was when he returned and put his foot on the step to get back in to his seat that he slipped and fell off on to the ground. Oh dear, before I could do owt, the tractor and the spreader ran over him. I stopped the tractor straight away, but it was too late. The heavy spreader had gone right over him. I ran round to him immediately, but I could see that it was very serious. The spreader was full of manure and very heavy. Poor Dad, I think he must have been killed instantly.'

'Why,' I asked, 'did he jump off while the tractor was moving, why not stop the whole machine and clear the blockage, surely that would be safer?'

'Well, that's what Dad was like. He was always in a hurry, but that's not why he kept the machine going: you see if you pump the lever at the back of the spreader while it's running, it clears the blockage quicker. He could have stopped the tractor and left the muck spreader going. But there! That's how it happened.'

'You know, these farm machines can be very dangerous.'

In all of the factories that I used to visit, particular care was taken to avoid accidents. They all employed safety officers to see that operators were protected. On small presses that could crush a finger or hand, the press would not work until a protection guard had been pulled into place. On the very large presses Fisher Bendix used for pressing out stainless steel sinks and large car body parts, a barrier came down that thrust the operator right away from the danger area. Accidents did still happen: eye injuries because the worker had not put on protective goggles and similar mishaps. Sometimes the injury was caused by factory negligence; the case would go to court and I was sometimes summoned to give evidence.

Some of the machinery used by farm workers: tractor hydraulics, chain saws, circular saws and more are not covered by safety procedures in the same way as they are in factories. In my experience accidents were surprisingly few considering the powerful machines that are being used every day. Any GP would know when there was an emergency in his practice, because there were no hospital accident and emergency departments then and the first doctor to be called was nearly always the injured person's own doctor. There were the casualty departments in the hospitals but except in very serious injuries the GP would be first on the scene, and could deal with most of the non life threatening accidents even if later the patient was referred to hospital casualty. In that case it would be expected that the doctor would telephone to warn that he was sending an accident patient.

I was called one night at about 10 pm to a farm in the area. It was a case of fairly severe scalds, I was told. They were all young people in the party, for I think they were having a party. Whether it was drugs or alcohol that caused a young woman to get into a bath with very hot water, I do not know. She was a large young woman and came out of the bath very quickly, as red as a lobster! Fortunately the burns were mild first degree, like sunburn; there would be no ulceration or severe tissue damage later; she was lucky to get away with it.

Unlike the lad operating a grass cutter with a horizontally rotating blade, who for some impulsive reason put his hand underneath. He lost the end of his right index finger. He didn't need to attend casualty, I was able to dress the wound.

On another occasion, I had just come into the house at coffee time when a young man whom I had not seen before came to the door. He was out of breath after running to the house.

'There's been an accident,' he shouted, 'down by the council houses at Thrimby, that steeply sloping field on the corner. I was just walking on the road there, you know where I mean,' he said, 'when I heard shouts and looking up, I saw two young men driving a tractor on the sloping ground there. As I watched, I could see that they were in a dangerous position. They were attempting to drive across the slope of the field. While I was watching the tractor keeled over. It was like a slow motion film. It looked as if those two men were going to be crushed under the tractor, but somehow they managed to jump clear, and the tractor fell on its side. One of the young men landed on a piece of outcrop rock. He may be injured, you'd better come down there now.'

'Come with me in the car, it'll be quicker,' I said.

We soon arrived at the spot and found that one of the young men had hit his head on the rock on which he had fallen. He had a laceration on the right side of his head and it was bleeding, but otherwise he seemed to be unhurt.

He got to his feet: 'Ow, I've hurt me 'ead, it's bleedin', look!'

'You'll have to come back to the house, get in the car,' I said. 'I'll have to see to that wound of yours.'

I took them all back to the Long House and examined the laceration. It wasn't serious. I washed it clean and inserted two sutures. I realised what a lucky escape they'd had.

'Now, what were you doing with that tractor on the sloping field? Surely you shouldn't have been driving it there?'

'It's me dad's tractor,' said the older lad. 'He's got some yows (ewes) in that field that need feed. He said to take the turnips on the trailer. We'd dropped the trailer with the turnips and were heading back. It was when we were turning the tractor that it happened. One of the wheels slipped into a rut and the whole bloody thing started to keel over.'

I examined him briefly to make sure there were no other injuries. 'You are lucky, you seem to have got away with what could have been a very serious accident.'

'What's your name?' I asked.

'I'm Tom Bowes, and this is my mate Gareth.'

'Oh I see, you're Willie Bowes' son from Hidesdale Hall, Great Strickland are you?'

'Aye, that's reet,' said he.

'I'll take you back home, and we'll explain to your father what has happened. He'll have to get some help getting that tractor back upright. Get in the car, lads.'

I thanked the man who had alerted us. He was on his way to Towcett to pick up his car. I offered him a lift, but he declined saying he would enjoy the walk.

When we arrived at Mr Bowes' farm, he was in the yard dealing with some calves. When he saw us he looked worried and hurried over to the car. 'Where have you two lads been?' Then he saw the plaster on Tom's head.

'What the hell has happened to you, Tom, and where the dickens have you been? You left here two hours ago. Where's the bloody tractor?'

I intervened: 'I think they've had a lucky escape actually, Will.' I explained what had happened.

'It looks as if they were lucky to get away with superficial injuries when the tractor overturned and luckily threw them off. I don't think Gareth has been hurt at all, and Tom's injury is superficial, but I'm afraid you'll have to go with some help to get the tractor upright again, but I don't think it's damaged at all. It just lurched on its side and the boys were quick enough to jump off in time.'

'Well thanks for your help doctor, and by the way, who was the man who saw it and alerted you?' asked Will.

'I'm sorry, I haven't the faintest idea, he was on his way walking to Towcett, he said, to pick up his car. Perhaps he's a friend of Hugh's, he didn't say.'

13
Country Partnership

Accidents could and did happen fairly often. When an accident, happened that was not severe enough to telephone 999 for an emergency ambulance, the GP would nearly always be summoned first. I had just arrived home for lunch one day when the telephone rang.

'Doctor, it's Mrs Evans from Reagill – my daughter Jane has had an accident. I'm afraid she's fallen. She climbed a ladder to save a fledgling that had fallen from its nest under the gutter. She was climbing down the ladder when she missed her foot on the rung. She put out her right hand to try to break her fall and I think she has damaged her wrist. It's very painful, it looks as if she could have broken it and she is rather shaken. She's sitting down inside the house now. Could you come to see her please?'

'I'll be with you in twenty minutes or so. Just put her arm in a comfortable position and give her a cup of tea. I'm on my way.'

I knew very well where the family lived. They had moved up to Cumbria from Essex eight years before and had settled down happily to village life. Jane was the eldest of three children. They had all attended Appleby Grammar school and had all done very well. Jane was a grammar school teacher. It was a little odd that all the children and their mother appeared to be northern in their speech but Mr Evans had a marked Essex accent.

I arrived at the house and found Jane sitting in a chair by the fire. She was supporting her injured right wrist in her left hand.

'Hullo Jane, I am sorry to see you've hurt yourself. Now then, let's have look at your wrist.'

The wrist, just proximal to the carpal bones was a little swollen and very tender.

'Ow! that hurts,' she cried. 'Is it broken?'

'I'm afraid it likely is,' I replied. 'But tell me, how did you manage to miss your footing on the rung of the ladder, was it slippery?'

'No, I don't think so, I just seemed to be unable to control my leg.'

'That's just it,' her mother exclaimed. 'I've been noticing her walking, she often seems to trip because she doesn't lift her right foot up far enough, and she sometimes sways to the side when she's trying to sit down on a chair. It's just as if she is not controlling her movements!'

At this point I was beginning to wonder what was causing this poor coordination of Jane's movements.

'Have you ever had any trouble with your vision?' I asked.

'No, I've got very good eyesight,' she said. 'I don't use specs.'

'Have you ever had double vision,' I asked, 'you know just for a short time, seeing two of everything?'

'Yes she has,' said her mother. 'I remember very well, several years ago over a period of a few days, when Jane was a student. She asked me: "Why am I seeing double" I'd forgotten about that. Why do you mention that?'

'Well, it might be relevant' I said. 'Jane, would you just do the same as I'm doing.' I stretched my right arm out sideways with the tip of my index finger extended. Then I moved my arm in slowly with my eyes closed and touched the tip of my nose. This is a rough test of her coordination with the out-stretched finger to nose test.

'Will you have a go at doing that, Jane?'

This test is based on the fact that the body receives feed back information from the joints of the limbs which tells the brain exactly what position the limb is in. This is called proprioception. So in the test, if Jane stretched out her arm sideways she should be able to slowly move her arm in and touch the tip of her nose with her index finger and with her eyes closed. Jane's finger wobbled as she tried to touch the tip of her nose with her outstretched finger, and ended on her upper lip; she didn't quite touch her nose.

The history of double vision combined with the lack of coordination raised alarm bells within me. Apart from her injured wrist, it was going to be necessary for this patient to be investigated by a neurologist to determine if her symptoms were due to multiple sclerosis. I didn't want to alarm her parents at this stage, but I explained to Mrs Evans that it would be necessary to refer Jane to a specialist to find out just why she was having these problems of coordinating her movements. That in-coordination could have caused her foot to miss the ladder rung.

'I must send Jane to the Cumberland Infirmary to have an X-ray of her wrist, and I will write to the specialist to get an appointment for a check up on her nervous system.'

Mrs Evans looked at me in some alarm. 'What do you think is wrong, doctor, is it something serious you are suggesting?'

'There is no point in my speculating as I am not at all sure. I would rather get an expert opinion on this lack of coordination that seems to be present, before I say any more. I will keep in touch with you and if I get any news from the specialist I will talk to you at once.'

In truth I, like Jane's mother, was alarmed, but at this stage I did not want to alarm her more than that. The superficial tests I had carried out certainly pointed to multiple sclerosis. This is a disease of the white matter in the nervous system in which the myelin sheath that coats nerves in the brain and spinal cord is depleted. Myelin is composed of lipids and protein, it is an electric insulator which facilitates the passage of nerve impulses. The effect of de-myelinisation is to diminish the function of these nerves. The cause of the disease is thought to be due to a defect in the immune system: an auto immune disease. The most recent treatment consists of replacement of stem cells to replace the deficiency. There are in the region of 100,000 cases in the UK. I have had a patient who used cannabis to relieve some of the symptoms. I know of no firm evidence which supports this line of treatment, but there are many multiple sclerosis sufferers who declare that cannabis has helped them.

For some reason, in Shap we had more than our fair share of this disease which should be in the order of one patient per thousand people in Britain. The condition is almost absent in equatorial regions. In Shap, whose population was just over one thousand, I had four or five patients suffering from the disease; more than our fair share, statistically. I noticed that some patients very quickly progressed to a point where they had to use a wheelchair to get around, but others seemed to be able to carry on fairly normal lives with occasional bouts of symptoms. It was said at the time that there were various forms of the disease, some were remitting and recurring, some mild and some severe.

Jane attended the casualty department in Carlisle and her fractured wrist was immobilised with a dorsal slab of plaster. There was no displacement of the bones; it was a cracked radius bone, the forearm bone on the thumb side. She was referred to a medical consultant and saw him very shortly after that. He wrote to me saying that there was evidence of retrobulbar neuritis of the optic nerve and that in his opinion it was strong evidence that she was suffering from multiple sclerosis. He did add that he felt that she would have to retire from teaching quite soon! I did have a long discussion with Jane's parents and put the most optimistic outlook that I could. Over the next ten years Jane continued teaching, suffering relapses from time to time. I saw her frequently during this period and her spirits remained high. The nature of the relapses though made it quite clear that the cause was multiple sclerosis.

There is a more cheerful end to the story: Long after I had retired I met Jane in the town. She was looking well and told me that she had retired from teaching at the age of 62, having served forty years in the profession. When I saw her, she was walking normally but I thought that perhaps her speech was a little slurred.

There was only one way that a patient could contact me, apart from calling at the house, that was the telephone. But with no answer 'phone and no mobile phone I could not be summoned if I was out visiting patients. Latterly I had a pager. It would buzz to tell me to contact surgery or home in an emergency.

During surgery hours I answered all calls personally, put through to me by the receptionist, even though it sometimes meant interrupting a consultation. It saved time because I could answer a query at once, and I discouraged long conversations! Apart from surgery hours all calls came through to home where Marjorie took messages and tried to sort out problems where possible. This, I believe was the usual arrangement in small practices then.

Some patients would call at the house at a time they knew I would be there. Many times I arrived home at lunchtime or after evening surgery and Marjorie would say to me as I came through the door: 'There's a man waiting to see you in the hall' – the room at the south end of the house I kept for such occasions. I never was quite sure when I might be summoned, except when it was my time off and my partner was on call.

Latterly when I was a little older and after I had retired to bed feeling more than a little tired, I would look at the telephone by my bedside and wish I could cast a spell on it to keep it quiet so that I could have an undisturbed night. I mostly did enjoy quiet nights after midnight. But I was all too frequently called out at 2 am on a freezing cold early morning, dragged from the depths of sleep; like being hauled out of a warm clinging embrace, only to face the reality of a night call, the properties of which would not be really known until I had seen and spoken to the patient.

I was often tempted to try to assuage the anxieties of a caller by listening, advising and reassuring, where I thought that to make a visit could wait until the morning. If I did persuade the patient that a visit was not necessary at so late an hour, I would be unable to get back to sleep due to worry that I had made a mistake. Sometimes I put off going on a call only to lie awake unable to sleep until I had changed my mind and made the visit after all. Sometimes when this happened, when I arrived at the house, the patient or the caller would say: 'Oh I am sorry you've come, after all, I think everything is OK. I shouldn't have bothered you. Can I make you a cup of tea?'

I am sorry to say that there have been many instances reported in the media where a GP should have visited, but did not, with very severe consequences; particularly when the sick patient was a child. Sometimes such a visit involved a journey through the snow to an uncertain or difficult to find house. I found that doing night calls became increasingly unpleasant as I grew older.

I remember on one occasion, in the Lincolnshire practice when I was just a beginner, a parent phoned me in the very early morning. She was just asking for advice; not wanting me to visit a child who was complaining of abdominal pain. I insisted on getting up and going to see the child. I was young, and it was a novelty! I was also concerned not to make a mistake. If a person is tired after a long bout of demanding physical or mental work, mistakes are more likely to be made. I am thinking just now of the junior doctors working excessively long hours. I know, I've been there, as have most doctors! It is no wonder that the modern GP uses 'out of hours' call service. But that service is not popular with patients, so they often go to accident end emergency instead.

There was no out of hours service for me at 2 am on one Wednesday night in January. It had been snowing heavily all the previous day, but I had had no problem getting around in the four wheel drive Subaru. The telephone woke me out of a deep sleep. I was dreaming of my home in Wales and I had been trying to stalk and shoot rabbits on my uncle's farm as I had been wont to do in my youth. The bang of the gun as it went off woke me suddenly and I found that I had knocked the telephone on to the floor. It was ringing loudly. I fumbled for it and eventually managed to pick it up.

'Hello' said a man's voice, 'is that the doctor?'

'Yes, who is it?'

'Oh, good, I'm sorry Doc to call you at this time. It's Eric Hodges speaking. I'm afraid I'm in trouble and I need your help.'

'Hullo Eric, what's the matter?'

'I think there's something seriously wrong in me belly.'

'Go on then, tell me what's happening, are you in pain.'

'Aye and it's summat awful, I can tell thee. I've got bad pains in me stomach, I can't pass 'owt in'toilet, and now a'm bringin' up some foul smellin' puke.'

'Oh dear, I'm sorry to hear that, it sounds bad. All right Eric, I'm coming. When did it all start?'

'A'll tell thee when ah see thee.'

It was a very cold night and I left Marjorie peacefully sleeping with a faint snuffling noise. I put on warm clothing and went out to the car. When I opened the garage door from the inside, I was pleased to see that although it had snowed heavily yesterday, the snow had been compressed on the road by the farm vehicles. The Subaru started immediately and I put it into four wheel drive and backed it out on to the road. It was icy, and very slippery so I had to go carefully. Eric had, since his retirement lived in a small cottage, near Maulds Meaburn. The going was a little hazardous because of the icy roads and at one point when I touched the brake I nearly went into a wall.

The road between Newby and Morland is narrow and winding and that night very icy as well. Thank goodness there were no other cars likely to be out at that time. It took me nearly half an hour to get to the turn into the lane to Eric's cottage. When I saw the state of the lane my heart sank! There had been no cars or tractors on it all of the day before and the snow was really deep. It was about a hundred and fifty yards to the cottage and I didn't fancy walking through the snow to get there although I was wearing wellington boots. The little four wheel drive Subaru tackled the deep snow gamely. Then suddenly we stopped; that is, the car stopped moving but the wheels were still turning. I had driven onto a deeper mound of snow which was frozen and the car was resting on frozen snow with the wheels barely touching the ground. I'd have to walk the rest of the way, that was clear. Only a few yards, but I was wondering how I was going to get off the deep frozen snow mound. I'd have to cross that bridge when I came to it. I went in at the back door calling: 'Hullo Eric, where are you?'

'Ah'm upstairs in't bedroom,' he shouted.

Up the narrow winding stairs of the cottage I went and found Eric in bed looking very anxious.

'Now then Eric, what's the matter? You said you'd explain. Well here I am, so tell me what's gone wrong.'

'Hello doctor, thanks for coming, I knew you would, 'cos I'm sure there's summat serious in my belly.

'Are you in pain?' I asked.

'It's like this,' he said. 'I went to Kendal on Monday to get some supplies. I took some bait (lunch) with me. I didn't want a big lunch, just some cheese and tomato sandwiches. I parked by Morrisons and bought all me shopping there. I sat in the car afterwards and ate me sandwiches. I'd hardly finished when I began to feel terrible sick. I got out of t'car and straight away, I was sick! I vomited all me lunch back and some nasty brown bitter stuff an all! I had a bit of pain in me belly too.

'After a bit, I began to feel just a bit better so I called in to see me cousin, she lives at Kendal y'know. She's a nurse at the hospital. I telled her what had happened and she said: "now look Eric, you could have got food poisoning, you go straight home and call the doctor! Can you drive d'you think?"

'Aye, Ahm aw'reet. So that were Monday, and yesterday the pain got a lot worse and it were coming in spasms, like, y'know colic. I didn't sleep much I can tell ye. I felt terrible sick and I vomited all this brown smelly stuff. It's in a basin downstairs by the door.'

I went downstairs and found the bowl with the vomit. It was obviously faecal material. This was going to be serious. I went back upstairs.

The writer and his wife Marjorie with Skippy the dog on an afternoon out.

'Eric, just lie flat and let me have look at your stomach.'

'What is this?' I asked. There was a large swelling in the region of his umbilicus – his navel.

'Is that where the pain is?'

'Aye, It's an umbiblical hernia.'

'An umbilical hernia, yes?'

'Whatever. I've alus had it'.

I palpated gently. It was hard, there were many bowel sounds coming from his abdomen when I listened with my stethoscope.

'Have you had a bowel movement in the last few days, or passed any wind?'

'No, I bin very costiv,' said he.

'Well Eric, you have a bowel obstruction, and it's quite serious, I'll have to get you into hospital immediately.'

'What'll happen to Ross, me dog?'

'I'll let your cousin from Crosby know and he'll come and take care of Ross. OK?'

241

Eric was in hospital within a couple of hours and they found a strangulated umbilical hernia. Marjorie and I went to see him and found him in intensive care, but doing well.

After seeing him and making arrangements for his admission, I returned to the car. Its warmth had melted the snow underneath and it was back on four wheels again, thank goodness. I was able to back it out down the lane and got home at 4 am. Very little sleep that night!

I was 61 on my next birthday at that time. I will not be able to do many night visits like this much longer I thought. Incidentally I noticed that my successor always had a day off following a long night visit. There were two doctors now running the surgery. In spite of that luxury I still felt I would rather work on my own, with a partner near by to share off duty. I was fortunate in having a partner who was cooperative and friendly: that was very important because it meant that we could always look forward and plan our holidays and time off. We spent most of our summer holidays exploring Europe in our caravan and we managed to tow our mobile home as far east as Hungary. But for short weekends in good weather we travelled around the Lake District and we felt lucky and happy to live and work in such pleasant surroundings among pleasant country folk.

14

Retirement, Now I am the Patient:
What seems to be the Problem?

This account is an attempt to describe what it was like for me 65 years ago working in General Practice. The NHS had just started and GPs were uncertain how it was going to develop. The parameters were laid down by Aneurin Bevan in the days when GPs prescribed or dispensed bottles of medicine and tubs of ointment. There were not so many drugs in the form of tablets and some older GPs were still rolling pills.

We as GPs then, had no access to clinical haematology, bacteriology or biochemistry. If we wanted to obtain a result of any of these clinical investigations, such as a blood sugar, haemoglobin or the bacteriology of an effusion, we had to make an appointment and send the patient to a consultant specialist clinic in the hospital. That is how it was in the practices I worked in at that time. Every day, in the surgery we saw patients with their problems and we attempted to sort them out either by prescribing a medicine or giving advice, or both. Also we dealt with minor accidents and carried out all the immunisations. Sometimes we attempted to help by talking and giving advice but patients often expected to be given 'a bottle'!

If all that was not enough we could refer the patient to a consultant clinic and of course there would be no charge for any of these services. My partner in the practice in Huyton repaired an inguinal hernia under local anaesthetic on the kitchen table; so he told me. Except in the case of very serious accidents we would not be expected to send a patient to casualty without making a prior appointment, or at least letting casualty know. Also in most cases we would be expected to send a letter giving all the details and the reason for the referral.

We were able to make use of the availability of a consultant domiciliary visit. I believe that today's GPs are much better informed than I was, and possibly have no need for this facility. I am not sure that the NHS could cope with this service now, in which consultants agreed to come out to the patient's home, discuss the problem in a relaxed way as if it were a private consultation. I, my partner and my colleagues certainly made use of this service fairly frequently, and the consultant in question was paid for his visit by the NHS.

During the 1950s and1960s, I asked several eminent consultant specialists on occasions to visit patients at home with me. There never seemed to be any problem or delay, they always seemed glad to help, and I benefited greatly on every occasion.

It was only gradually as time crept by into the 1960s that the pathology labs and X-ray departments opened their doors to GPs and allowed them to send in samples and receive the result direct without the patient attending a hospital outpatient clinic. There may have been exceptions, but I remember telling my cousin who was a consultant physician in South Wales: 'It's a great step forward, don't you think that I can now get a haemoglobin and full blood count done without sending the patient to hospital; I can even get an injured limb or a chest X-rayed, by sending the patient straight to the X-ray department.'

'Well,' he said, rather severely, 'I suppose that is all right, but I don't think you should have access to contrast radiography.' He was of course referring to such investigations as IVPs – intravenous pyelograms for investigating diseases of the kidneys, or barium meal X-rays for diagnosis of stomach ulcers and related conditions. Admittedly these specialist investigations were quite costly for the NHS, but to send the patient through the hospital clinics, taking the time of specialist consultants and ancillary staff would surely be more costly and time absorbing, and, at the same time the investigation would still be carried out. We, as students in the 1940s, were not as scientific as is the young doctor of today. Our teachers used to tell us often, in my experience that 'Medicine is an art not a science.' It was often said in addition, that it is a vocation, not a job. Of course there was an element of truth in it at that time!

According to the nineteenth century novelist, George Elliot who wrote a paper on 'The Safe Doctor', the most important subjects to study for a career in medicine prior to entering a medical school were the Classics and Botany! I remember a lady asking me how I had managed with my study of Greek.

We as students studied the sciences: physics, chemistry, biology and the medical branches of these pure sciences: biophysics, biochemistry and physiopathology, etc. But when it came to examining and treating patients the emphasis was on using our natural senses: the ear, hand and eye. Listen, listen, listen to what the patient is saying, we were told. Examine carefully, make a careful note of all your observations and make your diagnosis.

Professor Noble Chamberlain wrote a book which was the first clinical treatise that I bought, *Symptoms and signs in Clinical Medicine*. It was not a big book but it gave detailed directions on how to take a patient's history and how to physically examine. We all, or most of us as students, read it and it was most instructive. I doubt whether today's medical student will use it. I spoke to a young woman, my grand niece a few weeks after she had been admitted to medical school. Apparently, very early on in her class the students were brought into close contact with patients by sitting in on GPs' surgeries, she told me.

So the modern young doctor is more of a scientist than my generation were. They, I believe also study not only human science and disease and treatments but also human behaviour and medical ethics of which we knew almost nothing. When dealing with an ethical problem, we just used our common sense, but that is not sufficient today. The modern complicated procedures, for example: dealing with human embryos to try to help women to have a healthy baby and avoid an inherited gene fault has to be monitored carefully. The science of 'epi-genetics' is on the way up and with it will grow the philosophical study of medical ethics.

As I see it, the modern medical graduate is perfectly capable of specialisation today because the standard of academic qualifications necessary to enter medical school is so high. Only the students with the highest grades are admitted. So I believe that many who wish to specialise as opposed to entering general practice only fail to do so because they do not succeed in gaining a place on the 'ladder'. There is simply no vacancy for them there. Then he or she has to choose an alternative branch of medicine. According to the news media, there is a desperate shortage of General Practitioners and practices in certain areas have closed down.

When I qualified in January 1950 there was a large influx of ex-

Service doctors home after war service at the end of the Second World War. Many of them applied for and were appointed as junior registrars. I remember seeing a cartoon in a national newspaper at the time showing a hospital ward round, and gathered round the bed were, among the students, many registrars! All supposedly wanting to specialise and work their way up the system. Junior house appointments were fairly easy to come by unless you wanted a high profile job like the Professor of Medicine's houseman or even an obstetric job; then it was much more difficult, as I found out!

Assistantship appointments in general practice were not too difficult to come by, but the best ones were hugely oversubscribed. I applied for one in a country practice in Ashby de la Zouch in West Leicestershire. There were many, many applicants. The principal held a sort of garden party on the large lawn of his big house and among the guests were the applicants, I could not count or estimate the number of applicants, nor could I distinguish guest from applicant. I was never formally interviewed by the boss of the practice. He called each one of us into a small office, and paid our expenses for attending the event.

One GP I encountered at Bromborough, who was advertising for an assistant had a fairly typical attitude to the duties of an assistant in the practice, and he said to me: 'Yes, I'll take you on as my assistant, but you must understand that you will be responsible for all the night calls, and that I spend much of my time in the local factories wining and dining with the directors.' Those were his exact words over the telephone to me. Needless to say I did not apply for that job!

It was very difficult to get into a practice as an assistant with a view to becoming a partner, but by the middle of the 1960s the situation was beginning to change. When single-handed practitioners retired, the practice was advertised and a new doctor appointed by the Executive Council that dealt with the administration of general practices. Later it was the Family Practitioner Committee. I applied for one such practice due to a retirement vacancy. I thought it was an ideal situation, only to find that the three unconnected doctors working in the practice area did not get on with each other so they would not cooperate with each other. They were afraid of losing their patients – poached by a rival! The retiring GP told me that if he wanted an evening off duty or a day or two away, he had to find a locum to do his work. There were no mobile telephones then and answer phones were just making their appearance and were expensive.

By this time there were not so many single-handed practices. Larger group practices were forming and working from health centres. The existing partners would appoint the new doctor themselves. The old system where the doctor lived on the premises from which he or she practised was disappearing fast.

When I joined the practice at Shap it was into a partnership of four doctors, two in Kirkby Stephen, one in Orton and myself in Shap. But each one worked entirely independently as if he were a single-handed GP. The partnership simply served to ensure that time off and holidays were covered. It was also financially one unit. Later the practice split into two units. I was virtually single -handed in my day to day work, but with one partner to share time off it was excellent. I worked from premises that I owned and for me, it was an ideal situation. I could have gone on working like this for years. I had every other weekend free, but I was on call every night except for my half day – Thursday. My partner had his half day on Wednesday.

I was beginning to feel the strain of doing night calls. They did not occur so often after midnight, but I would see patients at home nearly every evening until nine or ten o'clock. I had one room in the house set up with an examination couch and a medicine cupboard. Most patients who came at that time of day had either had some sort of accident or there was a worrying situation. These days such patients would attend the nearest accident and emergency ward in hospital. I was not allowed to become a part-time doctor, as some do today. If I had been allowed to share my duty hours, especially after midnight, I could have worked several years more.

After I retired, I was, quite frequently asked to come back to the practice in Shap as a locum, just for a day or two. But on one occasion I stood in for the two partners for ten days. The two of them went on a skiing holiday. I was on my own as I was before I retired. There was a difference however: by that time there was a full on call system established between 6 pm and 8 am. All I had to do was operate the machine that transferred all the calls to Cumbria Health on Call. I could go back home knowing that I would not be called – what bliss! Bliss for me, but not for the patients, who would have to put up with a strange doctor in an emergency.

I notice that in some practices, around the country these days, doctors seem to come and go more frequently than used to happen. This must mean that there is less stability in the job. In the 1960s I attended several meetings where there were murmurs of strike action. I am, and I was, totally against this but not enough attention was paid to the reason for this unrest among GPs. We were at that time employed as independent contractors bound to being responsible for the patients on our list for 24 hours of every day throughout the whole year. I know of some practices that had quite a lot of partners, as many as eight or ten. In such cases there was ample opportunity to share working schedules giving reasonable time off duty. But such practices did not always run smoothly. There would be a 'pecking order' and the senior partner would normally have the most authority.

Twice in my life I was approached by a GP from such a practice, wanting to join me in Shap. I had been looking for a new partner consequent upon the sad death of my existing partner. In both cases the doctor in question was leaving an existing large practice. The reason for wanting to move in both instances, I was told, was because of 'infighting' in the practice.

People may wonder what could possibly cause two or more partners in a practice to be so unhappy as to wish to leave. One reason could be that a partner standing in for a colleague could have overridden a diagnosis made by his 'friend' and started alternative treatments, thus disparaging his colleague.

I have worked as a locum in inner city practices, then as an assistant in a rural practice then as a partner in an urban practice and lastly in a rural practice. The reason I moved on from a stable partnership was to achieve my goal of working in a rural environment. There is no doubt in my mind that each type of practice area has its pros and cons.

In the early days of the NHS it was expected that a GP would spend a great deal of time visiting patients in their homes. I remember being asked more than once: 'On your rounds, will you call in and see Mrs so and so?' It was assumed that the doctor would do his 'round' and call in on a number of patients. I was told in the 1980s that doctors should call routinely on all elderly patients even if they were not ill; and I think that we did, more or less do that then.

When I worked in Lincolnshire the practice area was large and patients were scattered. This was the 1950s and most patients did not possess a car. If the doctor was needed, he was sent for to call and see the patient at home. Modern GPs would be horrified: I regularly made fifteen to twenty house calls each day. When my boss was away the number more or less doubled. At the time of an epidemic, influenza, measles or other regular endemic diseases, visits would increase. Correspondingly attendance at the surgery was small and I must admit that most calls were repeat visits; short and sweet, collecting an empty medicine bottle to be refilled and a brief enquiry as to the patient's continuing state of health and possibly a blood pressure check, but we did keep an eye on elderly 'at risk' patients.

I think many GPs spent much of their life in the car, especially in country areas. That was rightly considered to be a waste of GP time and expertise.

I did thoroughly enjoy my life in general practice, especially my work as a country GP. My boss in Lincolnshire told me at the outset: 'When you call at a patient's house, whether it's a first visit or a routine repeat visit, go to the back door, knock and walk in: that's what is expected.' I felt very privileged at the close contact that was there between myself and patients, I do miss that, now that I am retired.

You cannot put the clock back; general practice, as it was then, 50 or 60 years ago was so different. There have been so many advances in medical science and today's GP has to keep up with all the day to day advances so that he or she can give the best advice, investigation and medication that is available to his or her patients. The increasing number of new drugs makes it essential to know the ones that react with each other and to be aware of patient's side effects or sensitivity to a particular drug.

I do not know how attractive this branch of medical practice is today to young graduates in medicine. But judging by the exodus of doctors from the service there is clearly either something wrong with their terms of service, or the life of a GP is not their idea of medical practice.

Obviously at the age of 91 I could not practice medicine now, even if I wanted to. But strangely I have to say that that even if I were half my present age I am not sure that general practice would be my choice as a medical doctor in today's world. Perhaps it would be if the job were in a very rural setting.

I must emphasise that all of the encounters with patients that I have written about here are based on actual consultations though of course the names are fictitious but the places where they occurred are broadly correct. These events are as near to being accurate as I can remember and they are certainly described as it was in the clinical atmosphere of the new NHS.

It was so different then!